MODERN NOVELISTS

Selected readings

THE GENERAL STUDIES LIBRARY
Edited by Percy Wilson CB

MODERN NOVELISTS

Selected readings from English fiction

selected by **D. L. B. Hartley** B Sc.(Econ.)

Senior History Master,
The Lakes School, Windermere

introduced by **Percy Wilson CB**

THAMES AND HUDSON · LONDON

I should like to thank Mr Percy Wilson, CB, MA, General Editor of the series, for his guidance during the preparation of this book. The suggestions and opinions of my colleagues Mr Denis Moorhouse, MA, and Mr J. M. Houston, BA, have helped a great deal; I am very grateful.

THAMES AND HUDSON LTD.
30–34 Bloomsbury Street, London W.C.1

Printed in Great Britain by Billing & Sons Limited, Guildford and London

Contents

Introduction by Percy Wilson   7

H. G. Wells
Miss Ann Veronica Stanley   from *Ann Veronica*   16
A Proposal of Marriage   from *The History of Mr Polly*   23

Joseph Conrad
The Journey Out   from *Heart of Darkness*   31

Arnold Bennett
A Historic Moment in Family Life   from *The Old Wives' Tale*   40
The Elephant   from *The Old Wives' Tale*   46

D. H. Lawrence
The Defeat of Miriam   from *Sons and Lovers*   51

James Joyce
The Grave of Boyhood   from *Portrait of the Artist as a Young Man*   63

Aldous Huxley
The Civilized Attitude   from *Crome Yellow*   72
Preparation for Life   from *Brave New World*   77

E. M. Forster
An Interrupted Evening with Friends   from *A Passage to India*   82

Rosamond Lehmann
Walking Home   from *Invitation to the Waltz*   92

Arthur Koestler
Rubashov's Arrest   from *Darkness at Noon*   95

L. P. Hartley
The Geography Lesson   from *The Shrimp and the Anemone*   103

Graham Greene
Young Pemberton   from *The Heart of the Matter*   111

Kingsley Amis
A Contribution to Knowledge   from *Lucky Jim*   115

William Golding
Hunting the Beast   from *Lord of the Flies*   122

Alan Sillitoe
Monday Morning   from *Saturday Night and Sunday Morning*   129

Iris Murdoch
The Butterfly   from *The Bell*   136

V. S. Naipaul
English Composition   from *A House for Mr Biswas*   144

Further Selected Readings: English   152

Selected Readings from American Fiction   154

Selected Readings in Translation   156

Books on the Modern Novel   158

Acknowledgements   159

Introduction

For the last hundred years, at least, the novel as a literary form has fulfilled for the reading public many of the functions of didactic and narrative poetry in earlier times, of dramatic poetry for the Elizabethans, and of epic poetry and the drama in Greece from the time of Homer to the end of the classical period. Aristotle claimed in the *Poetics* that poetry is 'more philosophical' than history. By poetry he meant, in the main, the dramatic poetry of Aeschylus, Sophocles and Euripides, but his principle, if true, could be applied also to Shakespeare and Marlowe as well as to the epic poetry of Virgil, Dante and Milton. Can it be applied also to modern fiction?

While it is often questionable what Aristotle meant by the terms he used in the *Poetics*, it has been assumed by many critics and teachers that what he said about 'poetry', as compared with 'history', is relevant—if it *is* true—to any literary form that takes an imaginative view of man's life in the world. Of course, one may say it is not true. It is arguable that history, the record and interpretation of past events, is more 'philosophical' and more valuable than an invented narrative with imaginary characters. Contemporary public taste shows some signs of holding this view as compared with the reading tastes of book buyers, and library users, before the war. History, biography, autobiography and travel are now immensely popular, to say nothing of science, economics, psychology and religion which perhaps do not enter into this particular argument. But imaginative prose fiction is still widely read, both in its popular form—a 'good story', regardless of deep psychological truth or literary art—and in its more refined form as a serious reflection of life, embodied in imagined characters and contained, more or less, within the framework of a narrative plot.

Certainly the time has not yet come, nor will it probably ever come, when readers, especially young and intelligent readers, cease to be

7

interested in imaginative fiction if it holds their attention, reflects and interprets their contemporary world and transports them to scenes, places and events that lie, at least in part, outside their own daily experience. The 'novel', from its first appearance in mediaeval Italy, perhaps earlier still, in later Latin literature, has fulfilled this role increasingly as epic poetry has declined and as the drama has waxed and waned, for all kinds of different reasons, at different periods of history. Shakespeare took many of his plots, not only from chronicles but also from Italian 'novels'.

The novel, like the epic poem and the drama, explores the variety of life: material, social and psychological—many would say moral and spiritual also. From the passages in this anthology the reader can move from the creeks and swamps of the West African coast to a prosperous home in a London suburb in the first years of this century, from British India in the 'twenties to a contemporary civic university only fifteen years ago. The modern novel, in particular, explores also the inner life of the mind and personality: here are intimations of what it feels like to be a sixteen-year-old girl in the Home Counties or an Indian boy in Trinidad. The novel, like the drama, can extend our understanding and deepen our compassion.

For the last fifty or sixty years, the period covered by this anthology, the writers' perspectives have been affected not only by changes in the external world but also by changes in the spirit of the age and by corresponding changes in the writers' own mental and emotional attitudes and in their systems of belief. The novel since before the first war has been a different structure from the massive and yet often dazzling creations of Dickens and Thackeray, George Eliot and the Brontes, Trollope and Hardy, to go no further back in time. Arnold Bennett and the early H. G. Wells are a sort of bridge. But even while Bennett was writing his best books, James Joyce was preparing works of imaginative fiction that eventually exploded the whole stylistic and psychological framework within which Dickens, Hardy and Bennett had worked. Many readers will still prefer Dickens, Hardy, Conrad and Bennett to Joyce and Virginia Woolf. Some will prefer Graham Greene and Miss Murdoch to any of the others. But these profound changes in the novel *have* occurred, and the reasons may be of interest to many readers of modern fiction.

To take the external world first. The inventions and capital investment of the industrial revolution from the early nineteenth century onwards resulted in vastly increased production in the second half of the century. And Britain, because she was a generation ahead of any other country in economic development, was prosperous and, in some ways, influential as never before. This prosperity—never perhaps as deeply rooted as it seemed, and never equitably or even reasonably distributed—engendered confidence, optimism and, certainly, complacency. Surely, it was thought, the standards of the middle-classes who epitomized all that was new in this successful society, must be valid. The country was governed by men with 'sound' ideas in business and religion. Queen Victoria had married an intelligent and industrious German and was busy bringing up a family of children on sensible lines. God, who had created the world in 4004 BC, was in his Heaven. Dr Arnold had shown the way in education: 'The study of language seems to me as if it was given for the very purpose of forming the human mind in youth; and the Greek and Latin languages seem the very instruments by which this is to be effected.' The British Empire grew until it covered a quarter of the earth's surface. The doctrine of free trade was—temporarily—swallowed whole. 'The country is once more getting rich,' wrote *The Spectator*. 'The money is filtering downwards to the actual workers.' Probably they believed this. And, indeed, though there was poverty and social squalor in abundance even sixty years ago, the fire had gone, in Britain at least, from the working-class movement, quenched or at least dowsed by glib promises of improvement under the existing order. 'The System', as E. M. Nicholson has called it in his recent book, had come to stay.

All these assumptions were questioned and savagely mauled by Dickens, and many of them by George Eliot and Mrs Gaskell also, as they were by Wells, Gissing and Priestley later. But as early as the 1850s a dissenting note became apparent not only in a few popular novelists, but among many thinkers and men of letters as different as Matthew Arnold, Newman, Ruskin, Carlyle and J. S. Mill. And, of course, the men of science had laid some dangerous fuses to the whole apparatus of conventional belief. If Charles Darwin was right, the world could not possibly have been created during one week in 4004 BC. Herbert Spencer thought it was more important to learn about things than about the names of things in ancient languages (not perhaps a profound thought or in any way a fair comparison). J. S. Mill, who was not wholly a conventional utilitarian, suggested nevertheless that to say you were interfering with a man's freedom 'for his own good' was not good enough—even though your motive was genuinely altruistic. In *Das Kapital*, Karl Marx predicted that the capitalist system carried with it the seeds of its own destruction.

It was easy for the prosperous Victorian majority to ignore these voices, and on the whole they did. But not for long. By 1900 all their social and political assumptions were brutally challenged. The 'admirable' Germans had emerged as military, naval, industrial and colonial competitors. One of the great political parties was split on the question of free trade. The Indians did not appear to appreciate the efforts and benefits of British rule. In one decade the proportion of unemployed workers had risen from one per cent to eleven per cent. Mrs Sidney Webb, writing of Charles Booth's survey of *Life and Labour in London* (1886), said: '. . . in the wealthiest and most productive city in the world a million and a quarter persons fell below what he called "The Poverty Line".' When the London dockers struck for their 'tanner an hour' in 1889 they marched through the West End; the clubmen of Pall Mall, looking through their windows, laughed at 'the great unwashed', but they had seen something to think about. I can myself remember that in 1909, when I first started school, things were very different indeed from what they are now in that small industrial town where I was born. There are glimpses of a poor and sordid under-belly to Victorian England even in the solid-seeming bourgeois world of Bennett's *Old Wives' Tale*. When England changed—for the better, surely, despite all our present troubles—the English novel changed with it. Whether this was also for the better or not is left for readers to judge. The opportunity was certainly there. Has it been seized?

Perhaps this question is premature, or otiose, for there were other forces at work more profound and powerful than economics and politics, perhaps more powerful even than pure science. In 1914, after a century of peace, with only small though cruel intermissions, the country entered a long and bloody war which not only drained her of her youth but also created a deep, traumatic shock. A million British men were killed, each having passed the test of youth and health. Orthodox patriotism was challenged, perhaps for the first time in our history. 'Sweet and seemly it is to die for one's country'? If you could see the agony of one who did not get his gas-mask on in time, wrote Wilfred Owen, and walk behind the wagon we flung him on—

> My friend, you would not tell with such high zest
> To children ardent for some desperate glory,
> The old Lie: Dulce et decorum est
> Pro patria mori.

In *Eminent Victorians*, published in 1918, Lytton Strachey examined sceptically, and none too accurately, the lives of four Victorians who had hitherto been beyond criticism. When his *Queen Victoria* was published, and sympathetically received, in 1921 it seemed that no one and nothing was sacred. Much of this destructive energy was wanton, ill-natured and ill-aimed. But the insights of depth psychology had come to stay. Freud and Jung were literary forces more real and permanent than Lytton Strachey, and their influence was to increase the questioning of reputations and façades. Some contemporary critics now claim to discern the lineaments of psychological analysis—not characterization alone, masterly as that was—in the novels of Dickens and George Eliot. Perhaps they are right: it is certainly there in Hardy. But from D. H. Lawrence onwards it came out 'into the open', as it had with Proust, and no contemporary English novel is conceivable without it. We laymen are children in such matters, and doubtless we are sometimes taken in by novelists who know as little as ourselves about the dark hidden streams of human nature. There is too, unfortunately, the exploiting as well as the understanding of sexual behaviour and sexual motivation. But to turn one's back on depth psychology is to leave almost the whole of modern fiction of the last generation unread, and that would certainly include some masterpieces as well as a great deal of rubbish.

Most serious modern novels are marked by uncertainty and pessimism, many by cynicism also. Their intelligent and often 'intellectual' authors tend for the most part to withdraw from the larger world—perhaps, compared with Milton, Swift and Pope, most authors always have done since the French Revolution—and to concentrate on exploring the sensibilities and motives of characters. This second development is particularly 'modern', for as the old precepts were broken down, and as man's world became more mechanized and more urban following the industrial revolution and other revolutions in science, the role of the individual and of the individual artist in society also changed. Two questions predominated: what was man's real nature, and how did man relate to the external world? The Romantic poets were perhaps the first to record the particular dissociation, or 'alienation', of modern man, but even Dostoevsky, in the mid-nineteenth century, was writing novels in which the individual character's inner experience became as important as his outward actions.

One result of this new preoccupation on the part of modern novelists with man's inner experience, this self-consciousness, was that a distinction arose between 'high-brow' and 'low-brow', between 'serious' and 'popular' fiction, a distinction which existed much less sharply in the middle nineteenth century. Many readers began to associate 'serious' literature with affectation, obscurity, and a certain kind of intellectual and social snobbery. In turn, the 'popular' novel was held in contempt by many serious students of literature and in fact by some novelists. Perhaps this has begun to change in the last few years. In any case, the younger readers can judge these things best, for they are most aware of the tastes, habits and sensibilities of their contemporary world.

The scope of this anthology is roughly from Wells to Naipaul. Wells is a good start, for he was impatient for the new and better order which science had put within our grasp. He wrote a hundred books, and most of his novels were used as vehicles for ideas of social and scientific progress. But he was an artist also, as *Kipps* and *The History of Mr Polly* show. I shall mention these books again later.

Wells and Henry James (who, as an American citizen, is not directly represented here) had a grudging admiration for one another, though their work and personalities were so different. Behind James was the disintegration of the comfortable, cultured, middle-class world that once looked as though it would last for ever. In other ways, too, James's novels were a portent of the future. He explored the consciousness of his characters more overtly and intricately than any of his predecessors in English or American fiction. This refinement of perception and analysis was reflected in his prose, full of qualifications and subsidiary clauses. Thus, at the very beginning of the century there was a major novelist who points forward, in some ways at least, to the characteristically modern novels of James Joyce and Virginia Woolf.

James Joyce, even in his earlier and more conventionally constructed stories, *Dubliners* and *Portrait of the Artist as a Young Man*, subordinated the wide horizons of the external world to the inner private world of the mind and the emotions. In *Ulysses*, his masterpiece, first published in Paris in 1922 by his friend Sylvia Beach, the inner world of the psyche takes control, not only the mind and the emotions but also the sub-conscious with its fantasies and myths, its private 'landscapes', physical and symbolic, its enigmatic code-signs and linguistic innovations and its absence of formal plot. His later work became almost unintelligible to some, but in *Ulysses* Joyce created what is for many readers, especially those who first meet it in their youth, one of the most remarkable and stimulating great books—great in breadth of reference, experience and understanding as well as in literary scale—in our language.

Virginia Woolf, so different in her background and in her literary methods from Joyce, was equally a founder of the 'stream of consciousness' in the novel. As with Joyce, the innovation took progressive charge of her work which, starting with the fairly conventional plots of *Mrs Dalloway* and *Night and Day*, ended in the stream of thoughts and impressions that constitute the dominant note of *To the Lighthouse*, and even more of *The Waves* and *The Years*. Perhaps her most charming fantasy is *Orlando*, which is recommended to any reader approaching her work for the first time. She is not directly represented in this anthology, for a page or two of any of her books is almost impossible to select and isolate as a significant specimen. The other outstanding figure from the 'Bloomsbury' age, E. M. Forster, is represented by an extract from his masterpiece, *A Passage to India*.

For many readers, old and young, the novels and short stories of D. H. Lawrence stand for the spirit and style of modern fiction, in its earlier stages, as no others do. His plots are recognizable as stories, his characters are drawn from ordinary life, and his dialogue, or much of it, is realistic at least on the surface. Here is no stream of consciousness but a portrait, grim and poetic simultaneously, of the lives and loves of mainly humbly-situated characters, caught in the grip of our industrial civilization or escaping to the deceitful promise of tropical and semi-tropical paradises in the Mediterranean or Australia or Mexico, and finding their problems, old or new, still with them. Lawrence was the first English novelist to bring sex right out into the open as, in his view, the major human passion and one from which he clearly believed all human vitality derives. It was a heady wine for those who were young just after the first war: perhaps not so heady for the young today. And yet his popularity endures; or is it now on the wane? Many who recognize his courage and originality are yet inclined to think he may have been over-rated as a novelist. Few would question his power as a poet, not only in his own poetry but in the delicate perception with which the characters of his stories are drawn and the emotional power with which they interact, even where the plot is unconvincing, as it often is. His travel books, especially *Sea and Sardinia*, are superb. His psychological tracts, for instance *Fantasia of the Unconscious*, are unbelievably silly. Dr F. R. Leavis has written about Lawrence with great perception.

Readers will see for themselves the different ways in which the later authors represented here have developed the innovations of their pre-decessors and contributed other developments themselves. A considerable stir was made at different times—perhaps still is—by Aldous Huxley, George Orwell and Evelyn Waugh. Graham Greene has had a very wide appeal for a whole generation. Iris Murdoch is perhaps the best known of a gifted constellation of women novelists who are now among the best-known names in contemporary fiction. But 'rankings' and potted verdicts are of little use to the reader and are distasteful to the editor or anthologist even as he makes them. Among my own favourites in modern fiction, as I shall admit in a moment, are (in addition to E. M. Forster) two authors who have never been in the front row of popularity. How much of these preferences is purely personal? How much of it could I sustain in a reasoned argument if I were asked? If readers of this anthology, and of the novels represented in it, are sufficiently interested to ask and answer such critical questions for themselves, this is one of the particular contributions that a study of literature can make to education. Others include the vast range of ideas, psychological, social and political that are raised by modern fiction, as well as the opportunity to explore such general issues as the range of permissible topics, the ethics of censorship, and the relationship of religious and ethical beliefs to imaginative art.

But pleasure as a motive for reading fiction is not to be ignored, and the reader's enjoyment is usually a necessary prelude to engaging his deepest feelings, even of pity and fear, and to setting his mind to work on the 'ideas' of a novel. Many of us have never believed that literature can be 'taught' like some other branches of learning. To 'teach' the novel seems especially absurd, and this is the last thing that the present collection of readings is intended to promote. The extracts ought not be to used as quarries for 'practical criticism'. They are no more than small portions of imaginative wholes and their first purpose is to bring to the notice of readers novels that they may or may not have heard of, have not yet read, and may feel eager to read if the extract has interested and pleased them. From this can flow as much or as little further thinking, reading and discussion as the reader or the teacher wishes and has time for: a mixture of private and corporate activity no different from what the best has always been in the humane education of young people. I know that this is how Mr Hartley would like his book used, and how he has used these and other readings himself in his own school.

Perhaps this book really needed no introduction beyond a simple statement of what it did for me when I read it. I think I was familiar with almost all the authors represented and with many, but not all, of the novels from which the readings are drawn. Some of the stories that I loved best, *Kipps* and *Mr Polly*, in particular, I hardly needed to be reminded of. Others I did, and it was a great pleasure to be sent back to them. It was a special pleasure, with Wells, Conrad and Bennett, to be sent back to books I had read with pupils in school many years ago; I envied and still envy the lot of those whose duty and pleasure it is to read imaginative literature with the young—the shared experience gives you back something more than any private reading ever gives. The consummate literary skill of Arnold Bennett at his best, and the immense stature of Conrad always, and of E. M. Forster often, seemed plainer to me than they had ever been before.

As for the middle and later authors of this period of fifty or sixty years, I had my hits and my misses, some of them unexpected. I found that Virginia Woolf had faded a little; and Lawrence also, more even than when I last read him a few years ago. Joyce was as masterful as ever. Evelyn Waugh was not as funny, in his funny books, as I remembered, but *Lucky Jim* was, though few of my own generation seem to think so. Some of the younger novelists baffle me—Iris Murdoch is one—and some others leave me cold. Two authors whom I enjoyed in my younger days, Rosamond Lehmann and L. P. Hartley, I liked even better than I remembered. Indeed, I wonder now why they have never been ranked by critics amongst the best. The youngest of all authors represented here, V. S. Naipaul, I enjoyed as much as if I were his own age.

These estimates and preferences are of no value to the reader, no value to anyone but myself. It is certain that younger readers will come to very different conclusions, and they are just as likely, more so in the contemporary world, to be right—if there is such a thing as 'right' in literary judgments. What a joy it would be to match judgment with them! I hope that teachers who use this book will find it so, and that the younger readers in school or college will themselves match their judgments one against another, in a spirit of shared pleasure and discovery rather than of competition in punditry.

PERCY WILSON

H G Wells

Herbert George Wells was born in 1866 at 47 High Street, Bromley, Kent, where his father had a hardware shop, and died in London in 1946. He was apprenticed to a draper, became a teacher and took a London degree in biology. He made a name as a writer with the publication in 1895 of his scientific romance *The Time Machine*. In the next fifty years he was to publish about a hundred books, half of them novels.

Wells probably attached most importance to those of his writings which expressed his social philosophy. He wrote of his hopes for mankind in these words. 'The oppression of incessant toil can surely be lifted from everyone, and the miseries due to a great multitude of infections and disorders of nutrition and growth cease to be a part of human experience. Few people are perfectly healthy nowadays except for brief periods of happiness, but the elation of physical well-being will some day be the common lot of mankind. And not only from physical evils will man be largely free. He will not be left with his soul tangled, haunted by monstrous and irrational fears and a prey to malicious impulse. From his birth he will breathe sweetness and generosity. . . . Before mankind lies the prospect not only of health but of magnanimity.' This better world, peopled by 'a graver humanity, stronger, more lovely, longer lived', was to be made by a wider use of the scientific method and its application to social questions.

Wells was an educator in the widest sense; several generations were inspired by him. He believed that an educated man should be familiar with the outlines of human history, have some knowledge of the biological nature of living creatures and of the way man lived in society. He offered the factual material in the famous trilogy *The Outline of History* (1920), *The Science of Life* (with his son G. P. Wells and Julian Huxley, 1931) and *The Work, Wealth and Happiness of Mankind* (1932).

Wells's conscious outlook and intention were scientific. His natural genius was literary, and novels like *Kipps* (1905), *Tono-Bungay* (1909), *Ann Veronica* (1909) and *The History of Mr Polly* (1910) are memorable for their characterization, sharp observation, their humour and insight. They were new and 'modern' because they looked at life from the standpoint of a very large and neglected class, the struggling and confused lower-middle class of clerks and shop assistants.

Before the term was used Wells wrote science fiction: indeed, he and Jules Verne may be regarded as the creators of modern science fiction. But he wrote before this sort of work had separated itself from the main stream of literature. Most of his scientific romances depend upon one basic discovery or invention which Wells, with his scientific background, is able to present very plausibly. In *The Time Machine* we have a machine which can convey its passenger through time; in *The Invisible Man* (1897) a substance which can make a man invisible; and in *The First Men in the Moon* (1901) a material opaque to gravitation.

H. G. Wells published his *Experiment in Autobiography* in 1934.

Ann Veronica   **Miss Ann Veronica Stanley**

This novel was published in 1909, ten years before women voted in parliamentary elections, and the events in it take place during the first decade of the century.

One Wednesday afternoon in late September Ann Veronica Stanley came down from London in a state of solemn excitement and quite resolved to have things out with her father that very evening. She had trembled on the verge of such a resolution before, but this time quite definitely she made it. A crisis had been reached, and she was almost glad it had been reached. She made up her mind in the train home that it should be a decisive crisis. It is for that reason that this novel begins with her there, and neither earlier nor later, for it is the history of this crisis and its consequences that this novel has to tell.

She had a compartment to herself in the train from London to Morning-side Park, and she sat with both her feet on the seat in an attitude that would certainly have distressed her mother to see and horrified her grandmother beyond measure; she sat with her knees up to her chin and her hands clasped before them, and she was so lost in thought that she discovered with a start, from a lettered lamp, that she was at Morningside Park, and thought she was moving out of the station, whereas she was only moving in. 'Lord!' she said. She jumped up at once, caught up a leather clutch containing note-books, a fat text-book, and a chocolate-and-yellow-covered pamphlet, and leaped neatly from the carriage, only to discover that the train was slowing down and that she had to traverse the full length of the platform past it again as the result of her precipitation. 'Sold again,' she remarked. 'Idiot!' She raged inwardly, while she walked along with that air of self-contained serenity that is proper to a young lady of nearly two-and-twenty under the eye of the world.

She walked down the station approach, past the neat, unobtrusive offices of the coal merchant and the house agent, and so to the wicket gate by the butcher's shop that led to the field path to her home. Outside the post office stood a no-hatted, blond young man in grey flannels, who was elaborately affixing a stamp to a letter. At the sight of her he became rigid and a singularly bright shade of pink. She made herself serenely unaware of his existence, though it may be it was his presence that sent her by the field detour instead of by the direct path up the Avenue.

'Umph!' he said, and regarded his letter doubtfully before consigning it to the pillar-box. 'Here goes,' he said. Then he hovered undecidedly for some seconds with his hands in his pockets and his mouth puckered to a whistle before he turned to go home by the Avenue.

Ann Veronica forgot him as soon as she was through the gate, and her face resumed its expression of stern preoccupation. 'It's either now or never,' she said to herself. . . .

Morningside Park was a suburb that had not altogether, as people say, come off. It consisted, like pre-Roman Gaul, of three parts. There was first the Avenue, which ran in a consciously elegant curve from the railway station into an undeveloped wilderness of agriculture, with big yellow brick villas on either side, and then there was the Pavement, the little clump of shops about the post office, and under the railway arch was a congestion of workmen's dwellings. The road from Surbiton and Epsom ran under the arch, and, like a bright fungoid growth in the ditch, there was now appearing a sort of fourth estate of little red-and-white rough-cast villas, with meretricious gables and very brassy window blinds. Behind the Avenue was a little hill, and an iron-fenced path went over the crest of this to a stile under an elm-tree, and forked there, with one branch going back into the Avenue again.

'It's either now or never,' said Ann Veronica again, ascending this stile. 'Much as I hate rows. I've either got to make a stand or give in altogether.'

She seated herself in a loose and easy attitude and surveyed the backs of the Avenue houses; then her eyes wandered to where the new red-and-white villas peeped among the trees. She seemed to be making some sort of inventory. 'Ye gods!' she said at last. '*What* a place!'

'Stuffy isn't the word for it.'

'I wonder what he takes me for?'

When presently she got down from the stile a certain note of internal conflict, a touch of doubt, had gone from her warm-tinted face. She had now the clear and tranquil expression of one whose mind is made up. Her back had stiffened, and her hazel eyes looked steadfastly ahead.

As she approached the corner of the Avenue the blond, no-hatted young man in grey flannels appeared. There was a certain air of forced fortuity in his manner. He saluted awkwardly. 'Hallo, Vee!' he said.

'Hallo, Teddy!' she answered.

He hung vaguely for a moment as she passed.

But it was clear she was in no mood for Teddys. He realized that he was committed to the path across the fields, an uninteresting walk at the best of times.

'Oh! dammit!' he remarked, 'dammit!' with great bitterness as he faced it.

Ann Veronica Stanley was twenty-one and a half years old. She had black hair, fine eyebrows, and a clear complexion; and the forces that had modelled her features had loved and lingered at their work and made them subtle and fine. She was slender, and sometimes she seemed tall, and walked and carried herself lightly and joyfully as one who commonly and habitually feels well, and sometimes she stooped a little and was preoccupied. Her lips came together with an expression between contentment and the faintest shadow of a smile, her manner was one of quiet reserve, and behind this mask she was wildly discontented and eager for freedom and life.

She wanted to live. She was vehemently impatient—she did not clearly know for what—to do, to be, to experience. And experience was slow in coming. All the world about her seemed to be—how can one put it?—in wrappers, like a house when people leave it in the summer. The blinds were all drawn, the sunlight kept out, one could not tell what colours these grey swathings hid. She wanted to know. And there was no intimation whatever that the blinds would ever go up or the windows or doors be opened, or the chandeliers, that seemed to promise such a blaze of fire, unveiled and furnished and lit. Dim souls flitted about her. Not only speaking but it would seem even thinking in undertones. . . .

During her schooldays, especially her earlier schooldays, the world had been very explicit with her, telling her what to do, what not to do, giving her lessons to learn and games to play and interests of the most suitable and various kinds. Presently she woke up to the fact that there was a considerable group of interests called being in love and getting married, with certain attractive and amusing subsidiary developments, such as flirtation and 'being interested' in people of the opposite sex. She approached this field with her usual liveliness of apprehension. But here she met with a check. These interests her world promptly, through the agency of schoolmistresses, older schoolmates, her aunt, and a number of other responsible and authoritative people, assured her she must on no account think about. Miss Moffatt, the history and moral instruction mistress, was particularly explicit upon this score, and they all agreed in indicating contempt and pity for girls whose minds ran on such matters, and who betrayed it in their conversation or dress or bearing. It was, in fact, a group of interests quite unlike any other group, peculiar and special, and one to be thoroughly ashamed of. Nevertheless Ann Veronica found it a difficult matter not to think of these things. However, having a considerable amount of pride, she decided she would disavow these undesirable topics and keep her mind away from them just as far as she could; but it left her at the end of her schooldays with that wrapped feeling I have described, and rather at loose ends.

The world, she discovered, with these matters barred, had no particular place for her at all, nothing for her to do, except a functionless existence varied by calls, tennis, selected novels, walks, and dusting in her father's house. She thought study would be better. She was a clever girl, the best of her year in the high school, and she made a valiant fight for Somerville or Newnham, but her father had met and argued with a Somerville girl at a friend's dinner-table, and he thought that sort of thing unsexed a woman. He said simply that he wanted her to live at home. There was a certain amount of disputation, and meanwhile she went on at school. They compromised at length on the science course at the Tredgold Women's College—she had already matriculated into London University from school—she came of age, and she bickered with her aunt for latch-key privileges on the strength of that and her season ticket. Shamefaced curiosities began to come back into her mind, thinly disguised as literature and art. She read voraciously, and presently, because of her aunt's censorship, she took to smuggling any books she thought might be prohibited instead of bringing them home openly, and she went to the theatre whenever she could produce an acceptable friend to accompany her. She passed her general science examination with double honours and specialized in science. She happened to have an acute sense of form and unusual mental lucidity, and she found in biology, and particularly in comparative anatomy, a very considerable interest, albeit the illumination it cast on her personal life was not altogether direct. She dissected well, and in a year she found herself chafing at the limitations of the lady B.Sc. who retailed a store of faded learning in the Tredgold laboratory. She had already realized that this instructress was hopelessly wrong and foggy—it is the test of the good comparative anatomist—upon the skull. She discovered a desire to enter as a student in the Imperial College at Westminster, where Russell taught, and go on with her work at the fountain head.

She had asked about that already, and her father had replied evasively: 'We'll have to see about that, little Vee; we'll have to see about that.' In that posture of being seen about the matter hung until she seemed committed to another session at the Tredgold College, and in the meantime a smaller conflict arose and brought the latch-key question, and in fact the question of Ann Veronica's position generally, to an acute issue.

In addition to the various business men, solicitors, civil servants, and widow ladies who lived in the Morningside Park Avenue, there was a certain family of alien sympathies and artistic quality, the Widgetts, with which Ann Veronica had become very friendly. Mr Widgett was a journalist and art critic, addicted to a greenish-grey tweed suit and 'art' brown ties; he smoked corn-cob pipes in the Avenue on Sunday morning, travelled third class to London by unusual trains, and openly despised golf. He occupied one of the smaller houses near the station. He had one son, who had been co-educated, and three daughters with particularly jolly red hair that Ann Veronica found adorable. Two of these had been her particular intimates at the high school, and had done much to send her mind exploring beyond the limits of the available literature at home. It was a cheerful, irresponsible, shamelessly hard-up family in the key of faded green and flattened purple, and the girls went on from the high school to the Fadden Art School and a bright, eventful life of art student dances, Socialist meetings, theatre galleries, talking about work, and even, at intervals, work; and ever and again they drew Ann Veronica from her sound persistent industry into the circle of these experiences. They had asked her to come to the first of the two great annual Fadden dances, the October one, and Ann Veronica had accepted with enthusiasm. And now her father said she must not go.

He had 'put his foot down', and said she must not go.

Going involved two things that all Ann Veronica's tact had been ineffectual to conceal from her aunt and father. Her usual dignified reserve had availed her nothing. One point was that she was to wear fancy dress in the likeness of a corsair's bride, and the other was that she was to spend whatever vestiges of the night remained after the dance was over in London with the Widgett girls and a select party in 'quite a decent little hotel' near Fitzroy Square.

'But, my dear!' said Ann Veronica's aunt.

'You see,' said Ann Veronica, with the air of one who shares a difficulty. 'I've promised to go. I didn't realize—I don't see how I can get out of it now.'

Then it was her father issued his ultimatum. He had conveyed it to her, not verbally, but by means of a letter, which seemed to her a singularly ignoble method of prohibition. 'He couldn't look me in the face and say it,' said Ann Veronica. 'But of course it's aunt's doing really.'

And thus it was that as Ann Veronica neared the gates of home she said to herself: 'I'll have it out with him somehow. I'll have it out with him. And if he won't——'

But she did not give even unspoken words to the alternative at that time.

The History of Mr Polly **A Proposal of Marriage**

Mr Polly was a drapery assistant. Johnson, the business-like cousin with whom he was staying, urged him to open a shop of his own with the £350 he had just inherited from his father. One day when cycling in the country Mr Polly had met Christabel, an attractive red-haired girl from a boarding school. They had met several times and he had fallen romantically in love with her. The meetings had ended with the cruel discovery that some of her schoolfellows, and perhaps Christabel herself, were laughing at him. In this passage we find Mr Polly a few days later visiting Mrs Larkins and her three daughters, Annie, Minnie and Miriam. 'Mr Polly' was published in 1910.

It is an illogical consequence of one human being's ill-treatment that we should fly immediately to another, but that is the way with us. It seemed to Mr Polly that only a human touch could assuage the smart of his humiliation. Moreover, it had, for some undefined reason, to be a feminine touch, and the number of women in his world was limited.

He thought of the Larkins family—the Larkins whom he had not been near now for ten long days. Healing people they seemed to him now— healing simple people. They had good hearts, and he had neglected them for a mirage. If he rode over to them he would be able to talk bosh, and laugh, and forget the whirl of memories and thoughts that was spinning round and round so unendurably in his brain.

'Law!' said Mrs Larkins, 'come in! You're quite a stranger, Elfrid!'

'Been seeing to business,' said the unveracious Polly.

'None of 'em ain't at 'ome, but Miriam's just out to do a bit of shopping. Won't let me shop, she won't, because I'm so keerless. She's a wonderful manager, that girl. Minnie's got some work at the carpet place. 'Ope it won't make 'er ill again. She's the loving delikit sort, is Minnie. . . . Come into the front parlour. It's a bit untidy, but you got to take us as you find us. Wot you been doing to your face?'

'Bit of a scraze with the bicycle,' said Mr Polly.

' 'Ow?'

'Trying to pass a carriage on the wrong side, and he drew up and ran me against a wall.'

Mrs Larkins scrutinized it. 'You ought to 'ave someone look after your scrazes,' she said. 'That's all red and rough. It ought to be cold-creamed. Bring your bicycle into the passage and come in.'

She 'straightened up a bit'. That is to say, she increased the dislocation of a number of scattered articles, put a work-basket on the top of several books, swept two or three dogs'-eared numbers of *The Lady's Own Novelist* from the table into the broken armchair, and proceeded to sketch together the tea-things with various such interpolations as: 'Law, if I ain't forgot the butter!' All the while she talked of Annie's good spirits and cleverness with her millinery, and of Minnie's affection, and Miriam's relative love of order and management. Mr Polly stood by the window uneasily, and thought how good and sincere was the Larkins' tone. It was well to be back again.

'You're a long time finding that shop of yours,' said Mrs Larkins.

'Don't do to be too precipitous,' said Mr Polly.

'No,' said Mrs Larkins, 'once you got it you got it. Like choosing a 'usband. You better see you got it good. I kept Larkins 'esitating two years, I did, until I felt sure of him. A 'ansom man 'e was as you can see by the looks of the girls, but 'ansom is as 'ansom does. You'd like a bit of jam to your tea I expect? I 'ope they'll keep *their* men waiting when the time comes. I tell them if they think of marrying, it only shows they don't know when they're well off. Here's Miriam.'

Miriam entered with several parcels in a net, and a peevish expression. 'Mother,' she said, 'you might 'ave prevented my going out with the net with the broken handle. I've been cutting my fingers with the string all the way 'ome.' Then she discovered Mr Polly and her face brightened.

"Ello, Elfrid!' she said. 'Where you been all this time?'

'Looking round,' said Mr Polly.

'Found a shop?'

'One or two likely ones. But it takes time.'

'You've got the wrong cups, Mother.'

She went into the kitchen, disposed of her purchases, and returned with the right cups. 'What you done to your face, Elfrid?' she asked, and came and scrutinized his scratches. 'All rough it is.'

He repeated his story of the accident, and she was sympathetic in a pleasant, homely way.

'You *are* quiet to-day,' she said as they sat down to tea.

'Meditatious,' said Mr Polly.

Quite by accident he touched her hand on the table, and she answered his touch.

'Why not?' thought Mr Polly, and looking up, caught Mrs Larkins' eye and flushed guiltily. But Mrs Larkins, with unusual restraint, said nothing. She made a grimace, enigmatical, but in its essence friendly.

Presently Minnie came in with some vague grievance against the manager of the carpet-making place about his method of estimating piece work. Her account was redundant, defective, and highly technical, but redeemed by a certain earnestness. 'I'm never within sixpence of what I reckon to be,' she said. 'It's a bit too 'ot.' Then Mr Polly, feeling that he was being conspicuously dull, launched into a description of the shop he was looking for and the shops he had seen. His mind warmed up as he talked.

'Found your tongue again,' said Mrs Larkins.

He had. He began to embroider the subject and work upon it. For the first time it assumed picturesque and desirable qualities in his mind. It stimulated him to see how readily and willingly they accepted his sketches. Bright ideas appeared in his mind from nowhere. He was suddenly enthusiastic.

'When I get this shop of mine I shall have a cat. Must make a home for a cat, you know.'

'What, to catch the mice?' said Mrs Larkins.

'No—sleep in the window. A venerable signor of a cat. Tabby. Cat's no good if it isn't tabby. Cat I'm going to have, and a canary! Didn't think of that before, but a cat and a canary seem to go you know. Summer weather I shall sit at breakfast in the little room behind the shop, sun streaming in the window to rights, cat on a chair, canary singing, and—Mrs Polly. . . .'

''Ello!' said Mrs Larkins.

'Mrs Polly frying an extra bit of bacon. Bacon singing, cat singing, canary singing, kettle singing. Mrs Polly——'

'But who's Mrs Polly going to be?' said Mrs Larkins.

'Figment of imagination, M'am,' said Mr Polly. 'Put in to fill up picture. No face to figure—as yet. Still, that's how it will be, I can assure you. I think I must have a bit of garden. Johnson's the man for a garden, of course,' he said, going off at a tangent, 'but I don't mean a fierce sort of garden. Earnest industry. Anxious moments. Fervous digging. Shan't go in for that sort of garden, M'am. No! Too much Back ache for me. My garden will be just a patch of 'sturtiums and sweet-pea. Red-bricked yard, cloths'-line. Trellis put up in odd time. Humorous wind vane. Creeper up the back of the house.'

'Virginia creeper?' asked Miriam.

'Canary creeper,' said Mr Polly.

'You *will* 'ave it nice,' said Miriam, desirously.

'Rather,' said Mr Polly. 'Ting-a-ling-a-ling. Shop!'

He straightened himself up, and they all laughed.

'Smart little shop,' he said. 'Counter, Desk. All complete. Umbrella stand. Carpet on the floor. Cat asleep on the counter. Ties and hose on a rail over the counter. All right.'

'I wonder you don't set about it right off,' said Miriam.

'Mean to get it exactly right, M'am,' said Mr Polly.

'Have to have a Tom cat,' said Mr Polly, and paused for an expectant moment. 'Wouldn't do to open shop one morning, you know, and find the window full of kittens. Can't sell kittens. . . .'

When tea was over he was left alone with Minnie for a few minutes, and an odd intimation of an incident occurred that left Mr Polly rather scared and shaken. A silence fell between them—an uneasy silence. He sat with his elbows on the table looking at her. All the way from Ease-wood to Stamton his erratic imagination had been running upon neat ways of proposing marriage. I don't know why it should have done, but it had. It was a kind of secret exercise that had not any definite aim at the time, but which now recurred to him with extraordinary force. He couldn't think of anything in the world that wasn't the gambit to a pro-posal. It was almost irresistibly fascinating to think how immensely a few words from him would excite and revolutionize Minnie. She was sitting at the table with a work-basket among the tea-things, mending a glove in order to avoid her share of clearing away.

'I like cats,' said Minnie, after a thoughtful pause. 'I'm always saying to Mother, I wish we 'ad a cat. But we couldn't 'ave a cat 'ere—not with no yard.'

'Never had a cat myself,' said Mr Polly. 'No!'

'I'm fond of them,' said Minnie.

'I like the look of them,' said Mr Polly. 'Can't exactly call myself fond.'

'I expect I shall get one some day. When about you get your shop.'

'I shall have my shop all right before long,' said Mr Polly. 'Trust me. Canary bird and all.'

She shook her head. 'I shall get a cat first,' she said. 'You never mean anything you say.'

'Might get 'em together,' said Mr Polly, with his sense of a neat thing outrunning his discretion.

'Why! 'ow do you mean?' said Minnie, suddenly alert.

'Shop and cat thrown in,' said Mr Polly in spite of himself, and his head swam, and he broke out into a cold sweat as he said it.

He found her eyes fixed on him with an eager expression. 'Mean to say —?' she began as if for verification. He sprang to his feet, and turned to the window. 'Little dog!' he said, and moved doorward hastily. 'Eating my bicycle tyre, I believe,' he exclaimed. And so escaped.

He saw his bicycle in the hall and cut it dead.

He heard Mrs Larkins in the passage behind him as he opened the front door.

He turned to her. 'Thought my bicycle was on fire,' he said. 'Outside. Funny fancy! All right reely. Little dog outside. . . . Miriam ready?'

'What for?'

'To go and meet Annie.'

Mrs Larkins stared at him. 'You're stopping for a bit of supper?'

'If I may,' said Mr Polly.

'You're a rum un,' said Mrs Larkins and called: 'Miriam!'

Minnie appeared at the door of the room looking infinitely perplexed. 'There ain't a little dog anywhere, Elfrid,' she said.

Mr Polly passed his hand over his brow. 'I had a most curious sensation. Felt exactly as though something was up somewhere. That's why I said Little Dog. All right now.'

He bent down and pinched his bicycle tyre.

'You was saying something about a cat, Elfrid,' said Minnie.

'Give you one,' he answered, without looking up. 'The very day my shop is opened.'

He straightened himself up and smiled reassuringly.

'Trust me,' he said.

When, after imperceptible manoeuvres by Mrs Larkins, he found himself starting circuitously through the inevitable recreation ground with

Miriam to meet Annie, he found himself quite unable to avoid the topic
of the shop that had now taken such a grip upon him. A sense of danger
only increased the attraction. Minnie's persistent disposition to accompany them had been crushed by a novel and violent and pungently expressed desire on the part of Mrs Larkins to see her do something in the
house sometimes. . . .

'You really think you'll open a shop?' said Miriam.

'I hate cribs,' said Mr Polly, adopting a moderate tone. 'In a shop there's
this drawback and that, but one *is* one's own master.'

'That wasn't all talk?'

'Not a bit of it.'

'After all,' he went on, 'a little shop needn't be so bad.'

'It's a 'ome,' said Miriam.

'It's a home.'

Pause.

'There's no need to keep accounts and that sort of thing if there's no
assistant. I daresay I could run a shop all right if I wasn't interfered with.'

'I should like to see you in your shop,' said Miriam. 'I expect you'd
keep everything tremendously neat.'

The conversation flagged.

'Let's sit down on one of those seats over there past that notice board,'
said Miriam, 'where we can see those blue flowers.'

They did as she suggested, and sat down in a corner where a triangular
bed of stock and delphinium brightened the asphalted traceries of the
recreation ground.

'I wonder what they call those flowers,' she said. 'I always like them.
They're handsome.'

'Delphicums and larkspurs,' said Mr Polly. 'They used to be in the park
at Port Burdock.'

'Floriferous corner,' he said approvingly.

He put an arm over the back of the seat, and assumed a more comfortable attitude. He glanced at Miriam, who was sitting in a lax thoughtful
pose with her eyes on the flowers. She was wearing her old dress. She
had not had time to change, and the blue tones of her old dress brought
out a certain warmth in her skin, and her pose exaggerated whatever was
feminine in her rather lean and insufficient body, and rounded her flat
chest delusively. A little line of light lay across her profile. The afternoon
was full of transfiguring sunshine, children were playing noisily in the
adjacent sandpit, some Judas trees were abloom in the villa gardens that

bordered the recreation ground, and all the place was bright with touches of young summer colour. It all merged with the effect of Miriam in Mr Polly's mind.

Her thought found speech. 'One did ought to be happy in a shop,' she said, with a note of unusual softness in her voice.

It seemed to him that she was right. One did ought to be happy in a shop. Folly not to banish dreams that made one ache of townless woods and bracken tangles and red-haired linen-clad figures sitting in dappled sunshine upon grey and crumbling walls and looking queenly down on one with clear blue eyes. Cruel and foolish dreams they were, that ended in one's being laughed at and made a mock of. There was no mockery here.

'A shop's such a respectable thing to be,' said Miriam thoughtfully.

'*I* could be happy in a shop,' he said.

His sense of effect had made him pause.

'If I had the right company,' he added.

She became very still.

Mr Polly swerved a little from the conversational ice-run upon which he had embarked.

'I'm not such a blooming Geezer,' he said, 'as not to be able to sell goods a bit. One has to be nosy over one's buying, of course. But I shall do all right.'

He stopped, and felt falling, falling through the aching silence that followed.

'If you get the right company,' said Miriam.

'I shall get that all right.'

'You don't mean you've got some one——?'

He found himself plunging.

'I've got some one in my eye this minute,' he said.

'Elfrid!' she said turning to him. 'You don't mean——'

Well, *did* he mean? 'I do!' he said.

'Not reely!' She clenched her hands to keep still.

He took the conclusive step.

'Well, you and me, Miriam, in a little shop, with a cat and a canary——'

He tried too late to get back to a hypothetical note. 'Just suppose it!'

'You mean,' said Miriam, 'you're in love with me, Elfrid?'

What possible answer can a man give to such a question but 'Yes!'

Regardless of the public park, the children in the sandpit, and everyone, she bent forward and seized his shoulder and kissed him on the lips. Something lit up in Mr Polly at the touch. He put an arm about her and kissed her back, and felt an irrevocable act was sealed. He had a curious feeling that it would be very satisfying to marry and have a wife—only somehow he wished it wasn't Miriam. Her lips were very pleasant to him, and the feel of her in his arm.

They recoiled a little from each other, and sat for a moment flushed and awkwardly silent. His mind was altogether incapable of controlling its confusions.

'I didn't dream,' said Miriam, 'you cared. Sometimes I thought it was Annie, sometimes Minnie——'

'Always I liked you better than them,' said Mr Polly.

'I loved you, Elfrid,' said Miriam, 'since ever we met at your poor father's funeral. Leastways I *would* have done if I had thought——You didn't seem to mean anything you said.'

'I can't believe it!' she added.

'Nor I,' said Mr Polly.

'You mean to marry me and start that little shop?'

'Soon as ever I find it,' said Mr Polly.

'I had no more idea when I came out with you——'

'Nor me.'

'It's like a dream.'

They said no more for a little while.

'I got to pinch myself to think it's real,' said Miriam. 'What they'll do without me at 'ome I can't imagine. When I tell them——'

For the life of him Mr Polly could not tell whether he was fullest of tender anticipations or regretful panic.

'Mother's no good at managing—not a bit. Annie don't care for house-work, and Minnie's got no 'ead for it. What they'll do without me I can't imagine.'

'They'll have to do without you,' said Mr Polly, sticking to his guns.

A clock in the town began striking.

'Lor!' said Miriam, 'we shall miss Annie, sitting 'ere and love-making.'

She rose and made as if to take Mr Polly's arm. But Mr Polly felt that their condition must be nakedly exposed to the ridicule of the world by such a linking, and evaded her movement.

Annie was already in sight before a flood of hesitation and terrors assailed Mr Polly.

'Don't tell anyone yet a bit,' he said.

'Only Mother,' said Miriam firmly.

Joseph Conrad

Joseph Conrad (Teodor Jozef Konrad Korzeniowski) was born in 1857 in Podolia, a Polish province then under Russian rule. His father, a landowner, was found guilty of complicity in the Polish nationalist movement and when Joseph was three years old the family was banished to Northern Russia. By the age of twelve Joseph was an orphan in the care of an uncle in Cracow.

Young Joseph was determined to go to sea and in 1874 he travelled to Marseilles to join his first ship. Ultimately he became a master in the British Merchant Navy and a naturalized British subject. He left the sea in 1894 and settled in England. He died at Bishopsbourne, Kent, in 1924.

Conrad did not begin to learn English till he was twenty-three. That he should become one of the great masters of English prose is one of the most remarkable feats in literary history. His first book, *Almayer's Folly*, was published in 1895. The critic Walter Allen writes: 'Of the novels, *Nostromo* is undoubtedly the finest; a good case could be made out for considering it the greatest novel in English of this century.'

Conrad drew on his experience of many lands and of twenty years at sea and his books have been read as adventure stories. They appeal as such, but they are much more. Conrad shows us man's nature as it is revealed in the desperate situation. He shows us man armed with his skills and, perhaps, loyalty to a few principles, pitted against the jungle, a typhoon, a sea of corruption. Usually the action takes place in a narrow physical setting: between walls of forest or mountain or, most extremely, aboard ship. Everything is significant. This

narrowness allows great coherence and concentration; a powerful expression of the
state of mind of the characters is made
possible.

Heart of Darkness **The Journey Out**

*Marlow the narrator has obtained a job as captain of a river steamer on the Congo
in the employment of a European company. The story is closely symbolic. 'The
equation between the farthest point of navigation and the culminating point of
Marlow's experience is typical of Conrad's method. The voyage is both into the
darkness of Africa and into the darkness of Marlow's thoughts' (Walter Allen).
The nearer Marlow approached to the ultimate evil of the dealer Kurtz the less
confidence he had in his own rather simple concepts of virtue, justice, honour.*

*In 1890 Conrad went to the Congo to take charge of a river steamer and from
'The Congo Diary' in* Last Essays *we know that* Heart of Darkness *(1902)
contains much autobiographical material. In the last quarter of the nineteenth
century the European powers were moving into Africa; by 1900 only Liberia
and Abyssinia remained independent. At the time of Conrad's visit the Belgians
were seeking rubber and ivory in the Congo; the exploitation of the native
population was frightful.*

'I left in a French steamer, and she called in every blamed port they have
out there, for, as far as I could see, the sole purpose of landing soldiers and
custom-house officers. I watched the coast. Watching the coast as it slips
by the ship is like thinking about an enigma. There it is before you—
smiling, frowning, inviting, grand, mean, insipid, or savage, and always
mute with an air of whispering, Come and find out. This one was almost
featureless, as if still in the making, with an aspect of monotonous grim-
ness. The edge of a colossal jungle, so dark-green as to be almost black,
fringed with white surf, ran straight, like a ruled line, far, far away along
a blue sea whose glitter was blurred by a creeping mist. The sun was fierce,
the land seemed to glisten and drip with steam. Here and there grayish-
whitish specks showed up clustered inside the white surf, with a flag
flying above them perhaps. Settlements some centuries old, and still no
bigger than pin-heads on the untouched expanse of their background.
We pounded along, stopped, landed soldiers; went on, landed custom-
house clerks to levy toll in what looked like a God-forsaken wilderness,

with a tin shed and a flag-pole lost in it; landed more soldiers—to take care of the custom-house clerks, presumably. Some, I heard, got drowned in the surf; but whether they did or not, nobody seemed particularly to care. They were just flung out there, and on we went. Every day the coast looked the same, as though we had not moved; but we passed various places—trading places—with names like Gran' Bassam, Little Popo; names that seemed to belong to some sordid farce acted in front of a sinister back-cloth. The idleness of a passenger, my isolation amongst all these men with whom I had no point of contact, the oily and languid sea, the uniform sombreness of the coast, seemed to keep me away from the truth of things, within the toil of a mournful and senseless delusion. The voice of the surf heard now and then was a positive pleasure, like the speech of a brother. It was something natural, that has its reason, that had a meaning. Now and then a boat from the shore gave one a momentary contact with reality. It was paddled by black fellows. You could see from afar the white of their eyeballs glistening. They shouted, sang; their bodies streamed with perspiration; they had faces like grotesque masks—these chaps; but they had bone, muscle, a wild vitality, an intense energy of movement, that was as natural and true as the surf along their coast. They wanted no excuse for being there. They were a great comfort to look at. For a time I would feel I belonged still to a world of straight-forward facts; but the feeling would not last long. Something would turn up to scare it away. Once, I remember, we came upon a man-of-war anchored off the coast. There wasn't even a shed there, and she was shelling the bush. It appears the French had one of their wars going on thereabouts. Her ensign dropped limp like a rag; the muzzles of the long six-inch guns stuck out all over the low hull; the greasy, slimy swell swung her up lazily and let her down, swaying her thin masts. In the empty immensity of earth, sky and water, there she was, incomprehensible, firing into a continent. Pop, would go one of the six-inch guns; a small flame would dart and vanish, a little white smoke would disappear, a tiny projectile would give a feeble screech—and nothing happened. Nothing could happen. There was a touch of insanity in the proceeding, a sense of lugubrious drollery in the sight; and it was not dissipated by somebody on board assuring me earnestly there was a camp of natives—he called them enemies!—hidden out of sight somewhere.

'We gave her her letters (I heard the men in that lonely ship were dying of fever at the rate of three a-day) and went on. We called at some more places with farcical names, where the merry dance of death and trade goes on in a still and earthy atmosphere as of an overheated catacomb; all along the formless coast bordered by dangerous surf, as if Nature herself had tried to ward off intruders; in and out of rivers, streams of death in life, whose banks were rotting into mud, whose waters, thickened into slime, invaded the contorted mangroves, that seemed to writhe at us in the extremity of an impotent despair. Nowhere did we stop long enough to get a particularized impression, but the general sense of vague and oppressive wonder grew upon me. It was like a weary pilgrimage amongst hints for nightmares.

'It was upward of thirty days before I saw the mouth of the big river. We anchored off the seat of the government. But my work would not begin till some two hundred miles farther on. So as soon as I could I made a start for a place thirty miles higher up.

'I had my passage on a little sea-going steamer. Her captain was a Swede, and knowing me for a seaman, invited me on the bridge. He was a young man, lean, fair, and morose, with lanky hair and a shuffling gait. As we left the miserable little wharf, he tossed his head contemptuously at the shore. "Been living there?" he asked. I said, "Yes." "Fine lot these government chaps—are they not?" he went on, speaking English with great precision and considerable bitterness. "It is funny what some people will do for a few francs a-month. I wonder what becomes of that kind when it goes up country?" I said to him I expected to see that soon. "So-o-o!" he exclaimed. He shuffled athwart, keeping one eye ahead vigilantly. "Don't be too sure," he continued. "The other day I took up a man who hanged himself on the road. He was a Swede, too." "Hanged himself! Why, in God's name?" I cried. He kept on looking out watchfully. "Who knows? The sun too much for him, or the country perhaps."

'At last we opened a reach. A rocky cliff appeared, mounds of turned-up earth by the shore, houses on a hill, others with iron roofs, amongst a waste of excavations, or hanging to the declivity. A continuous noise of the rapids above hovered over this scene of inhabited devastation. A lot of people, mostly black and naked, moved about like ants. A jetty projected into the river. A blinding sunlight drowned all this at times in a sudden recrudescence of glare. "There's your Company's station," said the Swede, pointing to three wooden barrack-like structures on the rocky slope. "I will send your things up. Four boxes did you say? So, Farewell."

'I came upon a boiler wallowing in the grass, then found a path leading up the hill. It turned aside for the boulders, and also for an undersized railway-truck lying there on its back with its wheels in the air. One was off. The thing looked as dead as the carcass of some animal. I came upon more pieces of decaying machinery, a stack of rusty rails. To the left a clump of trees made a shady spot, where dark things seemed to stir feebly. I blinked, the path was steep. A horn tooted to the right, and I saw the black people run. A heavy and dull detonation shook the ground, a puff of smoke came out of the cliff, and that was all. No change appeared on the face of the rock. They were building a railway. The cliff was not in the way or anything; but this objectless blasting was all the work going on.

'A slight clinking behind me made me turn my head. Six black men advanced in a file, toiling up the path. They walked erect and slow, balancing small baskets full of earth on their heads, and the clink kept time with their footsteps. Black rags were wound round their loins, and the short ends behind waggled to and fro like tails. I could see every rib, the joints of their limbs were like knots in a rope; each had an iron collar on his neck, and all were connected together with a chain whose bights swung between them, rhythmically clinking. Another report from the cliff made me think suddenly of that ship of war I had seen firing into a continent. It was the same kind of ominous voice; but these men could by no stretch of imagination be called enemies. They were called criminals, and the outraged law, like the bursting shells, had come to them, an insoluble mystery from the sea. All their meagre breasts panted together, the violently dilated nostrils quivered, the eyes stared stonily up-hill. They passed me within six inches, without a glance, with that complete death-like indifference of unhappy savages. Behind this raw matter one of the reclaimed, the product of the new forces at work, strolled despondently, carrying a rifle by its middle. He had a uniform jacket with one button off, and seeing a white man on the path, hoisted his weapon to his shoulder with alacrity. This was simple prudence, white men being so much alike at a distance that he could not tell who I might be. He was speedily reassured, and with a large, white, rascally grin, and a glance at his charge, seemed to take me into partnership in his exalted trust. After all, I also was a part of the great cause of these high and just proceedings.

'Instead of going up, I turned and descended to the left. My idea was to let that chain-gang get out of sight before I climbed the hill. You know I am not particularly tender; I've had to strike and to fend off. I've had to resist and to attack sometimes—that's only one way of resisting—without counting the exact cost, according to the demands of such sort of life as I had blundered into. I've seen the devil of violence, and the devil of greed, and the devil of hot desire; but, by all the stars! these were strong, lusty, red-eyed devils, that swayed and drove men—men, I tell you. But as I stood on this hillside, I foresaw that in the blinding sunshine of that land I would become acquainted with a flabby, pretending, weak-eyed devil of a rapacious and pitiless folly. How insidious he could be, too, I was only to find out several months later and a thousand miles farther. For a moment I stood appalled, as though by a warning. Finally I descended the hill, obliquely, towards the trees I had seen.

'I avoided a vast artificial hole somebody had been digging on the slope, the purpose of which I found it impossible to divine. It wasn't a quarry or a sandpit, anyhow. It was just a hole. It might have been connected with the philanthropic desire of giving the criminals something to do. I don't know. Then I nearly fell into a very narrow ravine, almost no more than a scar in the hillside. I discovered that a lot of imported drain-pipes for the settlement had been tumbled in there. There wasn't one that was not broken. It was a wanton smash-up. At last I got under the trees. My purpose was to stroll into the shade for a moment; but no sooner within than it seemed to me that I had stepped into the gloomy circle of some Inferno. The rapids were near, and an uninterrupted, uniform, head-long, rushing noise filled the mournful stillness of the grove,where not a breath stirred, not a leaf moved, with a mysterious sound—as though the tearing pace of the launched earth had suddenly become audible.

'Black shapes crouched, lay, sat between the trees leaning against the trunks, clinging to the earth, half coming out, half effaced within the dim light, in all the attitudes of pain, abandonment, and despair. Another mine on the cliff went off, followed by a slight shudder of the soil under my feet. The work was going on. The work! And this was the place where some of the helpers had withdrawn to die.

'They were dying slowly—it was very clear. They were not enemies, they were not criminals, they were nothing earthly now—nothing but black shadows of disease and starvation, lying confusedly in the greenish gloom. Brought from all the recesses of the coast in all the legality of time contracts, lost in uncongenial surroundings, fed on unfamiliar food, they sickened, became inefficient, and were then allowed to crawl away and rest. These moribund shapes were free as air—and nearly as thin. I began to distinguish the gleam of the eyes under the trees. Then, glancing down, I saw a face near my hand. The black bones reclined at full length with one shoulder against the tree, and slowly the eyelids rose and the sunken eyes looked up at me, enormous and vacant, a kind of blind, white flicker in the depths of the orbs, which died out slowly. The man seemed young—almost a boy—but you know with them it's hard to tell. I found nothing else to do but to offer him one of my good Swede's ship's biscuits I had in my pocket. The fingers closed slowly on it and held—there was no other movement and no other glance. He had tied a bit of white worsted round his neck—Why? Where did he get it? Was it a badge—an ornament—a charm—a propitiatory act? Was there any idea at all connected with it? It looked startling round his black neck, this bit of white thread from beyond the seas.

'Near the same tree two more bundles of acute angles sat with their legs drawn up. One, with his chin propped on his knees, stared at nothing, in an intolerable and appalling manner: his brother phantom rested its forehead, as if overcome with a great weariness; and all about others were scattered in every pose of contorted collapse, as in some picture of a massacre or a pestilence. While I stood horror-struck, one of these creatures rose to his hands and knees, and went off on all-fours towards the river to drink. He lapped out of his hand, then sat up in the sunlight, crossing his shins in front of him, and after a time let his woolly head fall on his breastbone.

'I didn't want any more loitering in the shade, and I made haste towards the station. When near the buildings I met a white man, in such an unexpected elegance of get-up that in the first moment I took him for a sort of vision. I saw a high starched collar, white cuffs, a light alpaca jacket, snowy trousers, a clear necktie, and varnished boots. No hat. Hair parted, brushed, oiled, under a green-lined parasol held in a big white hand. He was amazing, and had a penholder behind his ear.

'I shook hands with this miracle, and I learned he was the Company's chief accountant, and that all the book-keeping was done at this station. He had come out for a moment, he said, "to get a breath of fresh air." The expression sounded wonderfully odd, with its suggestion of sedentary desk-life. I wouldn't have mentioned the fellow to you at all, only it was from his lips that I first heard the name of the man who is so indissolubly connected with the memories of that time. Moreover, I respected the fellow. Yes; I respected his collars, his vast cuffs, his brushed hair. His appearance was certainly that of a hairdresser's dummy; but in the great demoralization of the land he kept up his appearance. That's backbone. His starched collars and got-up shirt-fronts were achievements of character. He had been out nearly three years; and, later, I could not help asking him how he managed to sport such linen. He had just the faintest blush, and said modestly, "I've been teaching one of the native women about the station. It was difficult. She had a distaste for the work." Thus this man had verily accomplished something. And he was devoted to his books, which were in apple-pie order.

'Everything else in the station was in a muddle,—heads, things, buildings. Strings of dusty niggers with splay feet arrived and departed; a stream of manufactured goods, rubbishy cottons, beads, and brass-wire set into the depths of darkness, and in return came a precious trickle of ivory.

'I had to wait in the station for ten days—an eternity. I lived in a hut in the yard, but to be out of the chaos I would sometimes get into the accountant's office. It was built of horizontal planks, and so badly put together that, as he bent over his high desk, he was barred from neck to heels with narrow strips of sunlight. There was no need to open the big shutter to see. It was hot there, too; big flies buzzed fiendishly, and did not sting, but stabbed. I sat generally on the floor, while, of faultless appearance (and even slightly scented), perching on a high stool, he wrote, he wrote. Sometimes he stood up for exercise. When a truckle-bed with a sick man (some invalid agent from up-country) was put in there, he exhibited a gentle annoyance. "The groans of this sick person," he said, "distract my attention. And without that it is extremely difficult to guard against clerical errors in this climate."

'One day he remarked, without lifting his head, "In the interior you will no doubt meet Mr Kurtz." On my asking who Mr Kurtz was, he said he was a first-class agent; and seeing my disappointment at this information, he added slowly, laying down his pen, "He is a very remarkable person." Further questions elicited from him that Mr Kurtz was at present in charge of a trading post, a very important one, in the true ivory-country, at "the very bottom of there. Sends in as much ivory as all the others put together. . . ." He began to write again. The sick man was too ill to groan. The flies buzzed in a great peace.

'Suddenly there was a growing murmur of voices and a great tramping of feet. A caravan had come in. A violent babble of uncouth sounds burst out on the other side of the planks. All the carriers were speaking together, and in the midst of the uproar the lamentable voice of the chief agent was heard "giving it up" tearfully for the twentieth time that day. . . . He rose slowly. "What a frightful row," he said. He crossed the room gently to look at the sick man, and returning, said to me, "He does not hear." "What! Dead?" I asked, startled. "No, not yet," he answered, with great composure. Then, alluding with a toss of the head to the tumult in the station-yard, "When one has got to make correct entries, one comes to hate those savages—hate them to the death." He remained thoughtful for a moment. "When you see Mr Kurtz," he went on, "tell him from me that everything here"—he glanced at the desk—"is very satisfactory. I don't like to write to him—with those messengers of ours you never know who may get hold of your letter—at that Central Station." He stared at me for a moment with his mild, bulging eyes. "Oh, he will go far, very far," he began again. "He will be a somebody in the Administration before long. They, above—the Council in Europe, you know—mean him to be."

He turned to his work. The noise outside had ceased, and presently in going out I stopped at the door. In the steady buzz of flies the homeward-bound agent was lying flushed and insensible; the other, bent over his books, was making correct entries of perfectly correct transactions; and fifty feet below the doorstep I could see the still tree-tops of the grove of death.

'Next day I left that station at last, with a caravan of sixty men, for a two-hundred-mile tramp.'

Arnold Bennett

Arnold Bennett (1867–1931) was born and brought up near Hanley in Staffordshire. He first worked in a solicitor's office, but moved into journalism in his early twenties. In 1902, when he was thirty-five, Bennett went to live in Paris, confident of his ability to earn a living by writing. He married a Frenchwoman and lived in France till 1908.

He wrote many novels, short stories and plays. He attached great importance to efficiency, he was fascinated by problems of organization and wrote books with titles like *The Human Machine*, and *How to Live on Twenty-Four Hours a Day;* his last novel, *Imperial Palace*, published in 1930, is a study of the complex organization of a large luxury hotel. But Arnold Bennett was primarily a novelist of provincial life and many of his readers believe that of all his books *The Old Wives' Tale* (1908) and *Clayhanger* (1910) have the most durable qualities.

The Old Wives' Tale A Historic Moment in the Family Life

Constance and Sophia were the only children of Mr and Mrs Baines of St Luke's Square, Bursley in Staffordshire. The family lived above their shop, the best-known and most prosperous drapery in the town. The events in the following passage took place between 1863 and 1866, for we are told that 'half Lancashire was starving on account of the American War.' Constance, 16, and Sophia, 15, were 'exquisite, enchanting, artful, roguish, prim, gushing, ignorant and miraculously wise'. Sophia could not bear the idea of going into the shop, the future her parents had in mind for her. She wanted to be a teacher, but she had just been told that she was to leave school in the near future and that teaching was out of the question. 'No argument from her mother! No hearing even! Just a curt and haughty "Let me hear no more of this!" ' The girls shared a bedroom. Mr Povey who worked in the shop lived with the Baines family.

The next morning, early, Sophia stood gazing out of the window at the Square. It was Saturday, and all over the Square little stalls, with yellow linen roofs, were being erected for the principal market of the week. In those barbaric days Bursley had a majestic edifice, black as basalt, for the sale of dead animals by the limb and rib—it was entitled the 'Shambles'— but vegetables, fruit, cheese, eggs, and pikelets were still sold under canvas. Eggs are now offered at five farthings apiece in a palace that cost twenty-five thousand pounds. Yet you will find people in Bursley ready to assert that things generally are not what they were, and that in particular the romance of life has gone. But until it has gone it is never romance. To Sophia, though she was in a mood which usually stimulates the sense of the romantic, there was nothing of romance in this picturesque tented field. It was just the market. Holl's, the leading grocer's, was already open, at the extremity of the Square, and a boy apprentice was sweeping the pavement in front of it. The public-houses were open, several of them specializing in hot rum at 5.30 a.m. The town-crier, in his blue coat with red facings, crossed the Square, carrying his big bell by the tongue. There was the same shocking hole in one of Mrs Povey's (confectioner's) window-curtains—a hole which even her recent travail could scarcely excuse. Such matters it was that Sophia noticed with dull, smarting eyes.

'Sophia, you'll take your death of cold standing there like that!'

She jumped. The voice was her mother's. That vigorous woman, after a calm night by the side of the paralytic, was already up and neatly dressed. She carried a bottle and an egg-cup, and a small quantity of jam in a tablespoon.

'Get into bed again, do! There's a dear! You're shivering.'

White Sophia obeyed. It was true; she was shivering. Constance awoke. Mrs Baines went to the dressing-table and filled the egg-cup out of the bottle.

'Who's that for, mother?' Constance asked sleepily.

'It's for Sophia,' said Mrs Baines, with good cheer. 'Now, Sophia!' and she advanced with the egg-cup in one hand and the tablespoon in the other.

'What is it, mother?' asked Sophia, who well knew what it was.

'Castor-oil, my dear,' said Mrs Baines, winningly.

The ludicrousness of attempting to cure obstinacy and yearnings for a freer life by means of castor-oil is perhaps less real than apparent. The strange interdependence of spirit and body, though only understood intelligently in these intelligent days, was guessed at by sensible medieval mothers. And certainly, at the period when Mrs Baines represented modernity, castor-oil was still the remedy of remedies. It had supplanted cupping. And, if part of its vogue was due to its extreme unpleasantness, it had at least proved its qualities in many a contest with disease. Less than two years previously old Dr Harrop (father of him who told Mrs Baines about Mrs Povey), being then aged eighty-six, had fallen from top to bottom of his staircase. He had scrambled up, taken a dose of castor-oil at once, and on the morrow was as well as if he had never seen a staircase. This episode was town property and had sunk deep into all hearts.

'I don't want any, mother,' said Sophia, in dejection. 'I'm quite well.'

'You simply ate nothing all day yesterday,' said Mrs Baines. And she added, 'Come!' As if to say 'There's always this silly fuss with castor-oil. Don't keep me waiting.'

'I don't *want* any,' said Sophia, irritated and captious.

The two girls lay side by side, on their backs. They seemed very thin and fragile in comparison with the solidity of their mother. Constance wisely held her peace.

Mrs Baines put her lips together, meaning: 'This is becoming tedious. I shall have to be angry in another moment!'

'Come!' said she again.

The girls could hear her foot tapping on the floor.

'I really don't want it, mamma,' Sophia fought. 'I suppose I ought to know whether I need it or not.' This was insolence.

'Sophia, will you take this medicine, or won't you?'

In conflicts with her children, the mother's ultimatum always took the formula in which this phrase was cast. The girls knew, when things had arrived at the pitch of 'or won't you', spoken in Mrs Baines's firmest tone, that the end was upon them. Never had the ultimatum failed.

There was a silence.

'And I'll thank you to mind your manners,' Mrs Baines added.

'I won't take it,' said Sophia, sullenly and flatly; and she hid her face in the pillow.

It was a historic moment in the family life. Mrs Baines thought the last day had come. But still she held herself in dignity while the apocalypse roared in her ears.

'*Of course, I can't force you to take it,*' she said with superb evenness, masking anger by compassionate grief. 'You're a big girl and a naughty girl. And if you will be ill you must.'

Upon this immense admission, Mrs Baines departed.

Constance trembled.

Nor was that all. In the middle of the morning, when Mrs Baines was pricing new potatoes at a stall at the top end of the Square, and Constance choosing threepennyworth of flowers at the same stall, whom should they both see, walking all alone across the empty corner by the bank, but Sophia Baines! The Square was busy and populous, and Sophia was only visible behind a foreground of restless, chattering figures. But she was unmistakably seen. She had been beyond the Square and was returning. Constance could scarcely believe her eyes. Mrs Baines's heart jumped. For let it be said that the girls never under any circumstances went forth without permission, and scarcely ever alone. That Sophia should be at large in the town, without leave, without notice, exactly as if she were her own mistress, was a proposition which a day earlier had been inconceivable. Yet there she was, and moving with a leisureliness that must be described as effrontery!

Red with apprehension, Constance wondered what would happen. Mrs Baines said naught of her feelings, did not even indicate that she had seen the scandalous, the breath-taking sight. And they descended the Square laden with the lighter portions of what they had bought during an hour of buying. They went into the house by the King Street door; and the first thing they heard was the sound of the piano upstairs. Nothing happened. Mr Povey had his dinner alone; then the table was laid for them, and the bell rung, and Sophia came insolently downstairs to join her mother and sister. And nothing happened. The dinner was silently eaten, and Constance having rendered thanks to God, Sophia rose abruptly to go.

'Sophia!'

'Yes, mother.'

'Constance, stay where you are,' said Mrs Baines suddenly to Constance, who had meant to flee. Constance was therefore destined to be present at the happening, doubtless in order to emphasize its importance and seriousness.

'Sophia,' Mrs Baines resumed to her younger daughter in an ominous voice. 'No, please shut the door. There is no reason why everybody in the house should hear. Come right into the room—right in! That's it. Now, what were you doing out in the town this morning?'

Sophia was fidgeting nervously with the edge of her little black apron, and worrying a seam of the carpet with her toes. She bent her head towards her left shoulder, at first smiling vaguely. She said nothing, but every limb, every glance, every curve, was speaking. Mrs Baines sat firmly in her own rocking-chair, full of the sensation that she had Sophia, as it were, writhing on the end of a skewer. Constance was braced into a moveless anguish.

'I will have an answer,' pursued Mrs Baines. 'What were you doing out in the town this morning?'

'I just went out,' answered Sophia at length, still with eyes downcast, and in a rather simpering tone.

'Why did you go out? You said nothing to me about going out. I heard Constance ask you if you were coming with us to the market, and you said, very rudely, that you weren't.'

'I didn't say it rudely,' Sophia objected.

'Yes, you did. And I'll thank you not to answer back.'

'I didn't mean to say it rudely, did I, Constance?' Sophia's head turned sharply to her sister. Constance knew not where to look.

'Don't answer back,' Mrs Baines repeated sternly. 'And don't try to drag Constance into this, for I won't have it.'

'Oh, of course Constance is always right!' observed Sophia, with an irony whose unparalleled impudence shook Mrs Baines to her massive foundations.

'Do you want me to have to smack you, child?'

Her temper flashed out and you could see ringlets vibrating under the provocation of Sophia's sauciness. Then Sophia's lower lip began to fall and to bulge outwards, and all the muscles of her face seemed to slacken.

'You are a very naughty girl,' said Mrs Baines, with restraint. ('I've got her,' said Mrs Baines to herself. 'I may just as well keep my temper.')

And a sob broke out of Sophia. She was behaving like a little child. She bore no trace of the young maiden sedately crossing the Square without leave and without an escort.

('I knew she was going to cry,' said Mrs Baines, breathing relief.)

'I'm waiting,' said Mrs Baines aloud.

A second sob. Mrs Baines manufactured patience to meet the demand.

'You tell me not to answer back, and then you say you're waiting,' Sophia blubbered thickly.

'What's that you say? How can I tell what you say if you talk like that?' (But Mrs Baines failed to hear out of discretion, which is better than valour.)

'It's of no consequence,' Sophia blurted forth in a sob. She was weeping now, and tears ricocheting off her lovely crimson cheeks on to the carpet; her whole body was trembling.

'Don't be a great baby,' Mrs Baines enjoined, with a touch of rough persuasiveness in her voice.

'It's you who make me cry,' said Sophia bitterly. 'You make me cry and then you call me a great baby!' And sobs ran through her frame like waves one after another. She spoke so indistinctly that her mother now really had some difficulty in catching her words.

'Sophia,' said Mrs Baines, with god-like calm, 'it is not I who make you cry. It is your guilty conscience makes you cry. I have merely asked you a question, and I intend to have an answer.'

'I've told you.' Here Sophia checked the sobs with an immense effort.

'What have you told me?'

'I just went out.'

'I will have no trifling,' said Mrs Baines. 'What did you go out for, and without telling me? If you had told me afterwards, when I came in, of your own accord, it might have been different. But no, not a word! It is I who have to ask! Now, quick! I can't wait any longer.'

('I gave way over the castor-oil, my girl,' Mrs Baines said in her own breast. 'But not again! Not again!')

'I don't know,' Sophia murmured.

'What do you mean—you don't know?'

The sobbing recommenced tempestuously. 'I mean I don't know. I just went out.' Her voice rose; it was noisy, but scarcely articulate.'What if I did go out?'

'Sophia, I am not going to be talked to like this. If you think because you're leaving school you can do exactly as you like——'

'Do I want to leave school?' yelled Sophia, stamping. In a moment a hurricane of emotion overwhelmed her, as though that stamping of the foot had released the demons of the storm. Her face was transfigured by uncontrollable passion. 'You all want to make me miserable!' she shrieked with terrible violence. 'And now I can't even go out! You are a horrid, cruel woman, and I hate you! And you can do what you like! Put me in prison if you like! I know you'd be glad if I was dead!'

She dashed from the room, banging the door with a shock that made the house rattle. And she had shouted so loud that she might have been heard in the shop, and even in the kitchen. It was a startling experience for Mrs Baines. Mrs Baines, why did you saddle yourself with a witness? Why did you so positively say that you intended to have an answer?

'Really,' she stammered, pulling her dignity about her shoulders like a garment that the wind had snatched off. 'I never dreamed that poor girl had such a dreadful temper! What a pity it is, for her *own* sake!' It was the best she could do.

Constance, who could not bear to witness her mother's humiliation, vanished very quietly from the room. She got half-way upstairs to the second floor, and then, hearing the loud, rapid, painful, regular intake of sobbing breaths, she hesitated and crept down again.

This was Mrs Baines's first costly experience of the child thankless for having been brought into the world. It robbed her of her profound, absolute belief in herself. She had thought she knew everything in her house and could do everything there. And lo! she had suddenly stumbled against an unsuspected personality at large in her house, a sort of hard marble affair that informed her by means of bumps that if she did not want to be hurt she must keep out of the way.

The Old Wives' Tale   **The Elephant**

This passage illustrates what Mr J. B. Priestley calls the 'Old Dutch Master solidity' of the novel. Constance and Sophia are now eighteen and seventeen. Maggie was the Baines's maid. Mr Baines had been bedridden for fourteen years and was never to be left alone.

'Sophia, will you come and see the elephant? Do come!' Constance entered the drawing-room with this request on her eager lips.

'No,' said Sophia, with a touch of condescension. 'I'm far too busy for elephants.'

Only two years had passed; but both girls were grown up now; long sleeves, long skirts, hair that had settled down in life; and a demeanour immensely serious, as though existence were terrific in its responsibilities; yet sometimes childhood surprisingly broke through the crust of gravity, as now in Constance, aroused by such things as elephants, and proclaimed with vivacious gestures that it was not dead after all. The sisters were sharply differentiated. Constance wore the black alpaca apron and the scissors at the end of a long black elastic, which indicated her vocation in the shop. She was proving a considerable success in the millinery department. She had learnt how to talk to people, and was, in her modest way, very self-possessed. She was getting a little stouter. Everybody liked her.

Sophia had developed into the student. Time had accentuated her reserve. Her sole friend was Miss Chetwynd, with whom she was, having regard to the disparity of their ages, very intimate. At home she spoke little. She lacked amiability; as her mother said, she was 'touchy'. She required diplomacy from others, but did not render it again. Her attitude, indeed, was one of half-hidden disdain, now gentle, now coldly bitter. She would not wear an apron, in an age when aprons were almost essential to decency. No! She would *not* wear an apron, and there was an end of it. She was not so tidy as Constance, and if Constance's hands had taken on the coarse texture which comes from commerce with needles, pins, artificial flowers, and stuffs, Sophia's fine hands were seldom innocent of ink. But Sophia was splendidly beautiful. And even her mother and Constance had an instinctive idea that that face was, at any rate, a partial excuse for her asperity.

'Well,' said Constance, 'if you won't, I do believe I shall ask mother if she will.'

Sophia, bending over her books, made no answer. But the top of her head said: 'This has no interest for me whatever.'

Constance left the room, and in a moment returned with her mother.

'Sophia,' said her mother, with gay excitement, 'you might go and sit with your father for a bit while Constance and I just run up to the playground to see the elephant. You can work just as well in there as here. Your father's asleep.'

'Oh, very well!' Sophia agreed haughtily. 'Whatever is all this fuss about an elephant? Anyhow, it'll be quieter in your room. The noise here is splitting.' She gave a supercilious glance into the Square as she languidly rose.

It was the morning of the third day of Bursley Wakes; not the modern finicking and respectable, but an orgiastic carnival, gross in all its manifestations of joy. The whole centre of the town was given over to the furious pleasures of the people. Most of the Square was occupied by Wombwell's Menagerie, in a vast oblong tent, whose raging beasts roared and growled day and night. And spreading away from this supreme attraction, right up through the market-place past the town hall to Duck Bank, Duck Square and the waste land called the 'playground', were hundreds of booths with banners displaying all the delights of the horrible. You could see the atrocities of the French Revolution, and of the Fiji Islands, and the ravages of unspeakable diseases, and the living flesh of a nearly nude human female guaranteed to turn the scale at twenty-two stone, and the skeletons of the mysterious phantoscope, and the bloody contests of champions naked to the waist (with the chance of picking up a red tooth as a relic). You could try your strength by hitting an image of a fellow-creature in the stomach, and test your aim by knocking off the heads of other images with a wooden ball. You could also shoot with rifles at various targets. All the streets were lined with stalls loaded with food in heaps, chiefly dried fish, the entrails of animals, and gingerbread. All the public-houses were crammed, and frenzied jolly drunkards, men and women, lunged along the pavements everywhere, their shouts vying with the trumpets, horns, and drums of the booths, and the shrieking, rattling toys that the children carried.

It was a glorious spectacle, but not a spectacle for the leading families. Miss Chetwynd's school was closed, so that the daughters of leading families might remain in seclusion till the worst was over. The Baineses ignored the wakes in every possible way, choosing that week to have a show of mourning goods in the left-hand window, and refusing to let Maggie outside on any pretext. Therefore the dazzling social success of the elephant, which was quite easily drawing Mrs Baines into the vortex, cannot imaginably be over-estimated.

On the previous night one of the three Wombwell elephants had suddenly knelt on a man in the tent; he had then walked out of the tent and picked up another man at haphazard from the crowd which was staring at the great pictures in front, and tried to put this second man into his mouth. Being stopped by his Indian attendant with a pitchfork, he placed the man on the ground and stuck his tusk through an artery of the victim's arm. He then, amid unexampled excitement, suffered himself to be led away. He was conducted to the rear of the tent, just in front of Baines's shuttered windows, and by means of stakes, pulleys, and ropes, forced to his knees. His head was whitewashed, and six men of the Rifle Corps were engaged to shoot at him at a distance of five yards, while constables kept the crowd off with truncheons. He died instantly, rolling over with a soft thud. The crowd cheered, and, intoxicated by their importance, the Volunteers fired three more volleys into the carcass, and were then borne off as heroes to different inns. The elephant, by the help of his two companions, was got onto a railway lorry and disappeared into the night. Such was the greatest sensation that has ever occurred, or perhaps will ever occur, in Bursley. The excitement about the repeal of the Corn Laws, or about Inkerman, was feeble compared to that excitement. Mr Critchlow, who had been called on to put a hasty tourniquet round the arm of the second victim, had popped in afterwards to tell John

Baines all about it. Mr Baines's interest, however, had been slight. Mr Critchlow succeeded better with the ladies, who, though they had witnessed the shooting from the drawing-room, were thirsty for the most trifling details.

The next day it was known that the elephant lay near the playground, pending the decision of the chief bailiff and the medical officer as to his burial. And everybody had to visit the corpse. No social exclusiveness could withstand the seduction of that dead elephant. Pilgrims travelled from all the Five Towns to see him.

'We're going now,' said Mrs Baines, after she had assumed her bonnet and shawl.

'All right,' said Sophia, pretending to be absorbed in study, as she sat on the sofa at the foot of her father's bed.

And Constance, having put her head in at the door, drew her mother after her like a magnet.

Then Sophia heard a remarkable conversation in the passage.

'Are you going to see the elephant, Mrs Baines?' asked the voice of Mr Povey.

'Yes. Why?'

'I think I had better come with you. The crowd is sure to be very rough.' Mr Povey's tone was firm; he had a position.

'But the shop?'

'We shall not be long,' said Mr Povey.

'Oh, yes, mother,' Constance added appealingly.

Sophia felt the house thrill as the side-door banged. She sprang up and watched the three cross King Street diagonally, and so plunge into the wakes. This triple departure was surely the crowning tribute to the dead elephant! It was simply astonishing. It caused Sophia to perceive that she had miscalculated the importance of the elephant. It made her regret her scorn of the elephant as an attraction. She was left behind; and the joy of life was calling her. She could see down into the 'Vaults' on the opposite side of the street, where working men—potters and colliers—in their best clothes, some with high hats, were drinking, gesticulating, and laughing in a row at a long counter.

She noticed, while she was thus at the bedroom window, a young man ascending King Street, followed by a porter trundling a flat barrow of luggage. He passed slowly under the very window. She flushed. She had evidently been startled by the sight of this young man into no ordinary state of commotion. She glanced at the books on the sofa, and then at her father. Mr Baines, thin and gaunt, and acutely pitiable, still slept. His brain had almost ceased to be active now; he had to be fed and tended like a bearded baby, and he would sleep for hours at a stretch even in the daytime. Sophia left the room. A moment later she ran into the shop, an apparition that amazed the three young lady assistants. At the corner near the window on the fancy side a little nook had been formed by screening off a portion of the counter with large flower-boxes placed end-up. The corner had come to be known as 'Miss Baines's corner'. Sophia hastened to it, squeezing past a young lady assistant in the narrow space between the back of the counter and the shelf-lined wall. She sat down in Constance's chair and pretended to look for something. She had ex-amined herself in the cheval-glass in the showroom, on her way from the sick chamber. When she heard a voice near the door of the shop asking first for Mr Povey and then for Mrs Baines, she rose, and seizing the ob-ject nearest to her, which happened to be a pair of scissors, she hurried to-wards the showroom stairs as though the scissors had been a grail, passion-ately sought and to be jealously hidden away. She wanted to stop and turn round, but something prevented her. She was at the end of the counter, under the curving stairs, when one of the assistants said:

'I suppose you don't know when Mr Povey or your mother are likely to be back, Miss Sophia? Here's——'

It was a divine release for Sophia.

'They're—I—' she stammered, turning round abruptly. Luckily she was still sheltered behind the counter.

The young man whom she had seen in the street came boldly forward.

'Good morning, Miss Sophia,' said he, hat in hand. 'It is a long time since I had the pleasure of seeing you.'

Never had she blushed as she blushed then. She scarcely knew what she was doing as she moved slowly towards her sister's corner again, the young man following her on the customers' side of the counter.

D H Lawrence

David Herbert Lawrence was born at Eastwood, Nottinghamshire in 1885, the fourth child of a miner. He won a scholarship to Nottingham High School when he was thirteen. On leaving school he was first a clerk and then a pupil teacher. He took his teacher's certificate at Nottingham and taught for a short period in Croydon. He had started his first novel, *The White Peacock*, published in 1911, when he was a student; after leaving Croydon he lived entirely by writing.

For two years he travelled in Italy and Germany and, returning to England, was married in July 1914 to Frieda von Richthofen. In 1919 the Lawrences left England and travelled first in Europe and then in Australia and America. They settled for a while in New Mexico, but returned to Europe in 1929. Lawrence died of tuberculosis in 1930.

D. H. Lawrence was a poet and a prophet. His sensitivity and intuitive perception make the unique texture of his fiction. The deeper, unconscious levels of personal relationships are described. Lawrence believed that modern civilization had corrupted man's emotional life. H. G. Wells planned a better civilization. Lawrence had not the temperament for social analysis and planning, but would seek salvation in a freely flowing passionate life. He mistrusted the intellect; his dilemma was that he was himself an intellectual.

Sons and Lovers   The Defeat of Miriam

In a letter dated November 14, 1912, Lawrence wrote of Sons and Lovers, '. . . I *sent the MS of the Paul Morel novel to Duckworth, registered yesterday . . . . It follows this idea: a woman of character and refinement goes into the lower class, and has no satisfaction in her own life. She has had a passion for her husband, so the children are born of passion, and have heaps of vitality. But as her sons grow up she selects them as lovers—first the eldest, then the second. These sons are urged into life by their reciprocal love of their mother—urged on and on. But when they come to manhood, they can't love, because their mother is the strongest power in their lives, and holds them. . . . The next son (Paul) gets a woman who fights for his soul—fights his mother. The son loves the mother—all the sons hate and are jealous of the father. The battle goes on between the mother and the girl, with the son as object. . . . He is left in the end naked of everything, with the drift towards death. It is a great tragedy, and I tell you I have written a great book.' To a very large extent* Sons and Lovers *is autobiographical.*

Earlier in the evening while Beatrice, a friend of the family, and Miriam were in the house, Paul had neglected some bread which his mother had left in the oven. Annie was Paul's sister. He had walked home with Miriam and was himself now back home.

He was not home again until a quarter to eleven. His mother was seated in the rocking-chair, Annie, with a rope of hair hanging down her back, remained sitting on a low stool before the fire, her elbows on her knees, gloomily. On the table stood the offending loaf unswathed. Paul entered rather breathless. No one spoke. His mother was reading the little local newspaper. He took off his coat, and went to sit down on the sofa. His mother moved curtly aside to let him pass. No one spoke. He was very uncomfortable. For some minutes he sat pretending to read a piece of paper he found on the table. Then——

'I forgot that bread mother,' he said.

There was no answer from either woman.

'Well,' he said, 'it's only twopence ha'penny. I can pay you for that.'

Being angry he put three pennies on the table, and slid them towards his mother. She turned away her head. Her mouth was shut tightly.

'Yes,' said Annie, 'you don't know how badly my mother is!'

The girl sat staring into the fire.

'Why is she badly?' asked Paul, in his overbearing way.

'Well!' said Annie. 'She could scarcely get home.'

He looked closely at his mother. She looked ill.

'*Why* could she scarcely get home?' he asked her, still sharply. She would not answer.

'I found her as white as a sheet sitting here,' said Annie, with a suggestion of tears in her voice.

'Well, why?' insisted Paul. His brows were knitting, his eyes dilating passionately.

'It was enough to upset anybody,' said Mrs Morel, 'hugging those parcels—meat, and greengroceries, and a pair of curtains——'

'Well, why *did* you hug them; you needn't have done.'

'Then who would?'

'Let Annie fetch the meat.'

'Yes, and I *would* fetch the meat, but how was I to know? You were off with Miriam, instead of being in when my mother came.'

'And what was the matter with you?' asked Paul of his mother.

'I suppose it's my heart,' she replied. Certainly she looked bluish round the mouth.

'And have you felt it before?'

'Yes—often enough.'

'Then why haven't you told me?—and why haven't you seen a doctor?'

Mrs Morel shifted in her chair, angry with him for his hectoring.

'You'd never notice anything,' said Annie. 'You're too eager to be off with Miriam.'

'Oh am I—and any worse than you with Leonard?'

'*I* was in at a quarter to ten.'

There was silence in the room for a time.

'I should have thought,' said Mrs Morel bitterly,' that she wouldn't have occupied you so entirely as to burn a whole ovenful of bread.'

'Beatrice was here as well as she.'

'Very likely. But we know why the bread is spoilt.'

'Why?' he flashed.

'Because you were engrossed with Miriam,' replied Mrs Morel hotly.

'Oh, very well—then it was *not*!' he replied angrily.

He was distressed and wretched. Seizing a paper, he began to read. Annie, her blouse unfastened, her long ropes of hair twisted into a plait, went up to bed, bidding him a very curt goodnight.

Paul sat pretending to read. He knew his mother wanted to upbraid him. He also wanted to know what had made her ill, for he was troubled. So, instead of running away to bed, as he would have liked to do, he sat and waited. There was a tense silence. The clock ticked loudly.

'You'd better go to bed before your father comes in,' said the mother harshly. 'And if you're going to have anything to eat, you'd better get it.'

'I don't want anything.'

It was his mother's custom to bring in some trifle for supper on Friday night, the night of luxury for the colliers. He was too angry to go and find it in the pantry this night. This insulted her.

'If I *wanted* you to go to Selby on Friday night, I can imagine the scene,' said Mrs Morel. 'But you're never too tired to go if *she* will come for you. Nay, but you neither want to eat nor drink then.'

'I can't let her go alone.'

'Can't you? And why does she come?'

'Not because I ask her.'

'She doesn't come without you want her——'

'Well, what if I *do* want her——' he replied.

'Why, nothing, if it was sensible or reasonable. But to go trapesing up there miles and miles in the mud, coming home at midnight, and got to go to Nottingham in the morning——'

'If I hadn't you'd be just the same.'

'Yes, I should, because there's no sense in it. Is she *so* fascinating that you must follow her all that way?' Mrs Morel was bitterly sarcastic. She sat still, with averted face, stroking, with a rhythmic, jerked movement, the black sateen of her apron. It was a movement that hurt Paul to see.

'I do like her,' he said, 'but——'

'*Like* her!' said Mrs Morel, in the same biting tones. 'It seems to me you like nothing and nobody else. There's neither Annie, nor me, nor anyone now for you.'

'What nonsense, mother—you know I don't love her—I—I tell you I *don't* love her—she doesn't even walk with my arm, because I don't want her to.'

'Then why do you fly to her so often!'

'I *do* like to talk to her—I never said I didn't. But I don't love her.'

'Is there nobody else to talk to?'

'Not about the things we talk of. There's lots of things that you're not interested in, that——'

'What things?'

Mrs Morel was so intense that Paul began to pant.

'Why—painting—and books. *You* don't care about Herbert Spencer.'

'No,' was the sad reply. 'And *you* won't at my age.'

'Well, but I do now—and Miriam does——'

'And how do you know,' Mrs Morel flashed defiantly, 'that *I* shouldn't? Do you ever try me?'

'But you don't, Mother, you know you don't care whether a picture's decorative or not; you don't care what *manner* it is in.'

'How do you know I don't care? Do you ever try me? Do you ever talk to me about these things, to try?'

'But it's not that that matters to you, Mother, you know it's not.'

'What is it, then—what is it, then, that matters to me?' she flashed. He knitted his brows with pain.

'You're old, Mother, and we're young.'

He only meant that the interests of *her* age were not the interests of his. But he realized the moment he had spoken that he had said the wrong thing.

'Yes, I know it well—I am old. And therefore I may stand aside; I have nothing more to do with you. You only want me to wait on you—the rest is for Miriam.'

He could not bear it. Instinctively he realized that he was life to her. And, after all, she was the chief thing to him, the only supreme thing.

'You know it isn't, Mother, you know it isn't!'

She was moved to pity by his cry.

'It looks a great deal like it,' she said, half putting aside her despair.

'No, Mother—I really *don't* love her. I talk to her, but I want to come home to you.'

He had taken off his collar and tie, and rose, bare-throated, to go to bed. As he stooped to kiss his mother, she threw her arms round his neck, hid her face on his shoulder, and cried, in a whimpering voice, so unlike her her own that he writhed in agony:

'I can't bear it. I could let another woman—but not her. She'd leave me no room, not a bit of room——'

And immediately he hated Miriam bitterly.

'And I've never—you know, Paul—I've never had a husband—not really——'

He stroked his mother's hair, and his mouth was on her throat.

'And she exults so in taking you from me—she's not like ordinary girls.'

'Well, I don't love her, Mother,' he murmured, bowing his head and hiding his eyes on her shoulder in misery. His mother kissed him a long fervent kiss.

'My boy!' she said, in a voice trembling with passionate love.

Without knowing, he gently stroked her face.

'There,' said his mother, 'now go to bed. You'll be *so* tired in the morning.' As she was speaking she heard her husband coming. 'There's your father—now go.' Suddenly she looked at him almost as if in fear. 'Perhaps I'm selfish. If you want her, take her my boy.'

His mother looked so strange. Paul kissed her, trembling.

'Ha—Mother!' he said softly.

Morel came in, walking unevenly. His hat was over one corner of his eye. He balanced in the doorway.

'At your mischief again?' he said venomously.

Mrs Morel's emotion turned into sudden hate of the drunkard who had come in thus upon her.

'At any rate, it is sober,' she said.

'H'm—h'm! H'm—h'm!' he sneered. He went into the passage, hung up his hat and coat. Then they heard him go down three steps to the pantry. He returned with a piece of pork-pie in his fist. It was what Mrs Morel had bought for her son.

'Nor was that bought for you. If you can give me no more than twenty-five shillings, I'm sure I'm not going to buy you pork-pie to stuff, after you've swilled a bellyful of beer.'

'Wha-at—wha-at!' snarled Morel, toppling in his balance.

'Wha-at—not for me?' He looked at the piece of meat and crust, and suddenly, in a vicious spurt of temper, flung it into the fire.

Paul started to his feet.

'Waste your own stuff!' he cried.

'What—what!' suddenly shouted Morel, jumping up and clenching his fist. 'I'll show yer, yer young jockey!'

'All right!' said Paul viciously, putting his head on one side. 'Show me!'

He would at that moment dearly have loved to have a smack at something. Morel was half crouching, fists up, ready to spring. The young man stood, smiling with his lips.

'Ussha!' hissed the father, swiping round with a great stroke just past his son's face. He dared not, even though so close, really touch the young man, but swerved an inch away.

'Right!' said Paul, his eyes upon the side of his father's mouth, where in another instant his fist would have hit. He ached for that stroke. But he heard a faint moan from behind. His mother was deadly pale, and dark at the mouth. Morel was dancing up to deliver another blow.

'Father!' said Paul, so that the word rang.

Morel started, and stood at attention.

'Mother!' moaned the boy, 'Mother!'

She began to struggle with herself. Her open eyes watched him, although she could not move. Gradually she was coming to herself. He laid her down on the sofa, and ran upstairs for a little whisky, which at last she could sip. The tears were hopping down his face. As he kneeled in front of her he did not cry, but the tears ran down his face quietly. Morel, on the opposite side of the room, sat with his elbows on his knees glaring across.

'What's a-matter with 'er?' he asked.

'Faint!' replied Paul.

'H'm!'

The elderly man began to unlace his boots. He stumbled off to bed. His last fight was fought in that home.

Paul kneeled there, stroking his mother's hand.

'Don't be poorly, Mother—don't be poorly!' he said time after time.

'It's nothing, my boy,' she murmured.

At last he rose, fetched in a large piece of coal, and raked the fire. Then he cleared the room, put everything straight, laid the things for breakfast, and brought his mother's candle.

'Can you go to bed, Mother?'

'Yes, I'll come.'

'Sleep with Annie, Mother, not with him.'

'No, I'll sleep in my own bed.'

'Don't sleep with him, Mother.'

'I'll sleep in my own bed.'

She rose, and he turned out the gas, then followed her closely upstairs, carrying her candle. On the landing he kissed her close.

'Good night, Mother.'

'Good night!' she said.

He pressed his face upon the pillow in a fury of misery. And yet, somewhere in his soul, he was at peace because he still loved his mother best. It was the bitter peace of resignation.

The efforts of his father to conciliate him next day were a great humiliation to him.

Everybody tried to forget the scene.

Paul was dissatisfied with himself and with everything. The deepest of his love belonged to his mother. When he felt he had hurt her, or wounded his love for her, he could not bear it. Now it was spring, and there was battle between him and Miriam. This year he had a good deal against her. She was vaguely aware of it. The old feeling that she was to be a sacrifice to this love, which she had had when she prayed, was mingled in all her emotions. She did not at the bottom believe she ever would have him. She did not believe in herself primarily; doubted whether she could ever be what he would demand of her. Certainly she never saw herself living happily through a lifetime with him. She saw tragedy, sorrow, and sacrifice ahead. And in sacrifice she was proud, in renunciation she was strong, for she did not trust herself to support everyday life. She was prepared for the big things and the deep things, like tragedy. It was the sufficiency of the small day-life she could not trust.

The Easter holidays began happily. Paul was his own frank self. Yet she felt it would go wrong. On the Sunday afternoon she stood at her bedroom window, looking across at the oak-trees of the wood, in whose branches a twilight was tangled, below the bright sky of the afternoon. Grey-green rosettes of honeysuckle leaves hung before the window, some already, she fancied, showing bud. It was spring, which she loved and dreaded.

Hearing the clack of the gate she stood in suspense. It was a bright grey day, Paul came into the yard with his bicycle, which glittered as he walked. Usually he rang his bell and laughed towards the house. To-day he walked with shut lips and cold, cruel bearing, that had something of a slouch and a sneer in it. She knew him well by now, and could tell from that keen-looking, aloof young body of his what was happening inside him. There was a cold correctness in the way he put his bicycle in its place, that made her heart sink.

She came downstairs nervously. She was wearing a new net blouse that she thought became her. It had a high collar with a tiny ruff, reminding her of Mary Queen of Scots, and, making her, she thought, look wonderfully a woman, and dignified. At twenty she was full-breasted and luxuriously formed. Her face was still like a soft rich mask, unchangeable. But her eyes, once lifted, were wonderful. She was afraid of him. He would notice her new blouse.

He, being in a hard, ironical mood, was entertaining the family to a description of a service given in the Primitive Methodist Chapel, conducted by one of the well-known preachers of the sect. He sat at the head of the table, his mobile face, with eyes that could be so beautiful, shining with tenderness or dancing with laughter, now taking on one expression and then another, in imitation of various people he was mocking. His mockery always hurt her; it was too near the reality. He was too clever and cruel. She felt that when his eyes were like this, hard with mocking hate, he would spare neither himself nor anybody else. But Mrs Leivers was wiping her eyes with laughter, and Mr Leivers, just awake from his Sunday nap, was rubbing his head in amusement. The three brothers sat with ruffled sleepy appearance in their shirt-sleeves, giving a guffaw from time to time. The whole family loved a 'take-off' more than anything.

He took no notice of Miriam. Later, she saw him remark her new blouse, saw that the artist approved, but it won from him not a spark of warmth. She was nervous, could hardly reach the teacups from the shelves.

When the men went out to milk, she ventured to address him personally.

'You were late,' she said.

'Was I?' he answered.

There was silence for a while.

'Was it rough riding?' she asked.

'I didn't notice it.'

She continued quickly to lay the table. When she had finished——

'Tea won't be for a few minutes. Will you come and look at the daffodils?' she said.

He rose without answering. They went out into the back garden under the budding damson-trees. The hills and the sky were clean and cold. Everything looked washed, rather hard. Miriam glanced at Paul. He was pale and impassive. It seemed cruel to her that his eyes and brows, which she loved, could look so hurting.

'Has the wind made you tired?' she asked. She detected an underneath feeling of weariness about him.

'No, I think not,' he answered.

'It must be rough on the road—the wood moans so.'

'You can see by the clouds it's a south-west wind; that helps me here.'

'You see, I don't cycle, so I don't understand,' she murmured.

'Is there need to cycle to know that?' he said.

She thought his sarcasms were unnecessary. They went forward in silence. Round the wild, tussocky lawn at the back of the house was a thorn hedge, under which daffodils were craning forward from among their sheaves of grey-green blades. The cheeks of the flowers were greenish with cold. But still some had burst, and their gold ruffled and glowed.

Miriam went on her knees before one cluster, took a wild-looking daffodil between her hands, turned up its face of gold to her, and bowed down, caressing it with her mouth and cheeks and brows. He stood aside, with his hands in his pockets watching her. One after another she turned up to him the faces of the yellow, bursten flowers appealingly, fondling them lavishly all the while.

'Aren't they magnificent?' she murmured.

'Magnificent! it's a bit thick—they're pretty!'

She bowed again to her flowers at his censure of her praise. He watched her crouching, sipping the flowers with fervid kisses.

'Why must you always be fondling things!' he said irritably.

'But I love to touch them,' she replied, hurt.

'Can you never like things without clutching them as if you wanted to pull the heart out of them? Why don't you have a bit more restraint, or reserve, or something?'

She looked up at him full of pain, then continued slowly to stroke her lips against a ruffled flower. Their scent, as she smelled it, was so much kinder than he; it almost made her cry.

'You wheedle the souls out of things,' he said. 'I would never wheedle —at any rate, I'd go straight.'

He scarcely knew what he was saying. These things came from him mechanically. She looked at him. His body seemed one weapon, firm and hard against her.

'You're always begging for things to love you,' he said, 'as if you were a beggar for love. Even the flowers, you have to fawn on them——'

Rhythmically, Miriam was swaying and stroking the flower with her mouth, inhaling the scent which ever after made her shudder as it came to her nostrils.

'You don't want to love—your eternal and abnormal craving is to be loved. You aren't positive, you're negative. You absorb, absorb, as if you must fill yourself up with love, because you've got a shortage some-where.'

She was stunned by his cruelty, and did not hear. He had not the faintest notion of what he was saying. It was as if his fretted, tortured soul, run hot by thwarted passion, jetted off these sayings like sparks from electricity. She did not grasp anything he said. She only sat crouched beneath his cruelty and his hatred of her. She never realized in a flash. Over everything she brooded and brooded.

After tea he stayed with Edgar and the brother, taking no notice of

Miriam. She, extremely unhappy on this looked-for holiday, waited for him. And at last he yielded and came to her. She was determined to track this mood of his to its origin. She counted it not much more than a mood.

'Shall we go through the wood a little way?' she asked him, knowing he never refused a direct request.

They went down to the warren. On the middle path they passed a trap, a narrow horseshoe hedge of small fir-boughs, baited with the guts of a rabbit. Paul glanced at it frowning. She caught his eye.

'Isn't it dreadful?' she asked.

'I don't know? Is it worse than a weasel with its teeth in a rabbit's throat? One weasel or many rabbits? One or the other must go!'

He was taking the bitterness of life badly. She was rather sorry for him.

'We will go back to the house,' he said. 'I don't want to walk out.'

They went past the lilac-tree, whose bronze leaf-buds were coming unfastened. Just a fragment remained of the haystack, a monument squared and brown, like a pillar of stone. There was a little bed of hay from the last cutting.

'Let us sit here a minute,' said Miriam.

He sat down against his will, resting his back against the hard wall of hay. They faced the amphitheatre of round hills that glowed with sunset, tiny white farms standing out, the meadows golden, the woods dark and yet luminous, tree-tops folded over tree-tops, distinct in the distance. The evening had cleared, and the east was tender with a magenta flush under which the land lay still and rich.

'Isn't it beautiful?' she pleaded.

But he only scowled. He would rather have had it ugly just then.

At that moment a big bull-terrier came rushing up, open-mouthed, pranced his two paws on the youth's shoulders, licking his face. Paul drew back, laughing. Bill was a great relief to him. He pushed the dog aside, but it came leaping back.

'Get out,' said the lad, 'or I'll dot thee one.'

But the dog would not be pushed away. So Paul had a little battle with the creature, pitching poor Bill away from him, who, however, only floundered tumultuously back again, wild with joy. The two fought together, the man laughing grudgingly, the dog grinning all over. Miriam watched them. There was something pathetic about the man. He wanted so badly to love, to be tender. The tough way he bowled the dog over was really loving. Bill got up, panting with happiness, his brown eyes rolling in his white face, and lumbered back again. He adored Paul. The lad frowned.

'Bill, I've had enough o' thee,' he said.

But the dog only stood with two heavy paws, that quivered with love, upon his thigh, and flicked a red tongue at him. He drew back.

'No,' he said—'no—I've had enough.'

And in a minute the dog trotted off happily, to vary the fun.

He remained staring miserably across at the hills, whose still beauty he begrudged. He wanted to go and cycle with Edgar. Yet he had not the courage to leave Miriam.

'Why are you so sad?' she asked humbly.

'I'm not sad; why should I be?' he answered. 'I'm only normal.'

She wondered why he always claimed to be normal when he was disagreeable.

'But what is the matter?' she pleaded, coaxing him soothingly.

'Nothing!'

'Nay!' she murmured.

He picked up a stick and began to stab the earth with it.

'You'd far better not talk,' he said.

'But I wish to know——' she replied.

He laughed resentfully.

'You always do,' he said.

'It's not fair to me,' she murmured.

He thrust, thrust, thrust at the ground with the pointed stick, digging up little clods of earth as if he were in a fever of irritation. She gently and firmly laid her hand on his wrist.

'Don't!' she said. 'Put it away.'

He flung the stick into the currant-bushes, and leaned back. Now he was bottled up.

'What is it?' she pleaded softly.

He lay perfectly still, only his eyes alive, and they full of torment.

'You know,' he said at length, rather wearily—'you know—we'd better break off.'

It was what she dreaded. Swiftly everything seemed to darken before her eyes.

'Why?' she murmured. 'What has happened?'

'Nothing has happened. We only realize where we are. It's no good——'

She waited in silence, sadly, patiently. It was no good being impatient with him. At any rate, he would tell her now what ailed him.

James Joyce

James Joyce was born in Dublin in 1882 and died in Zurich in 1941. He was educated by the Jesuits at Sallins, County Kildare, and at University College, Dublin, where in 1902 he took a degree in modern languages. He left Ireland in 1904 and spent the rest of his life in Trieste, Paris and Zurich, writing prose and poetry and often earning a living by teaching and translating. All his life, in spite of poverty, periods of semi-blindness and difficulties with censors, he retained the agility, curiosity and sensibility of his youth.

Joyce wrote a play, *Exiles* (1918), and poetry. His best-known prose works are *Dubliners* (1914), *Portrait of the Artist as a Young Man* (1916), *Ulysses* (1922) and *Finnegans Wake* (1939).

As a young man he believed that Ireland put out a series of traps for the artist: language—the Gaelic language, nationalism and religion. Consequently he left Dublin— only to spend the rest of his life brooding upon it and writing about it.

It is claimed that Joyce has had great influence on subsequent novelists. Certainly he broke away from the traditional form. In 1920 Virginia Woolf in an essay on the modern novel in *The Common Reader* wrote, 'The writer seems constrained . . . to provide a plot, to provide comedy, tragedy, love interest. . . . Is life like this? Must novels be like this? Examine for a moment an ordinary day. The mind receives a myriad impressions—trivial, fantastic, evanescent or engraved with the sharpness of steel. Life is not a series of gig-lamps symmetrically arranged; life is a luminous halo, a semi-transparent envelope surrounding us from the beginning of consciousness to the end.' Joyce's novels, following the streams of consciousness of their characters, are the sort of work Virginia Woolf would expect from the liberated writer.

In *Portrait of the Artist as a Young Man* (1916) the whole action takes place in Stephen's consciousness. *Ulysses* is concerned with one day, 16 June 1904, in the lives of Stephen Dedalus, a poverty-stricken intellectual recently returned from Paris, and Leopold Bloom, an advertising space salesman. There is no plot, but it is pointed out that *Ulysses* follows the pattern of the *Odyssey*. *Finnegans Wake* is largely a scholar's book. The ordinary reader needs a key or commentary; nevertheless he will find it fascinating to dip into, for there is much comic word-play, and incidental poetry.

Portrait of the Artist as a Young Man

From the Grave of Boyhood

We are reading of the Jesuit education of Stephen Dedalus. The director of the school has recently asked Stephen if he had ever felt a vocation for the priesthood. '—To receive that call, Stephen, said the priest, is the greatest honour that the Almighty God can bestow upon a man. No king or emperor on this earth has the power of the priest of God.' This is a crucially important moment in Stephen's life and he will soon reach a decision.

He could wait no longer.

From the door of Byron's publichouse to the gate of Clontarf Chapel, from the gate of Clontarf Chapel to the door of Byron's publichouse, and then back again to the chapel and then back again to the publichouse he had paced slowly at first, planting his steps scrupulously in the spaces of the patchwork of the footpath, then timing their fall to the fall of verses. A full hour had passed since his father had gone in with Dan Crosby, the tutor, to find out for him something about the university. For a full hour he had paced up and down, waiting: but he could wait no longer.

He set off abruptly for the Bull, walking rapidly lest his father's shrill whistle might call him back; and in a few moments he had rounded the curve at the police barrack and was safe.

Yes, his mother was hostile to the idea, as he had read from her listless silence. Yet her mistrust pricked him more keenly than his father's pride and he thought coldly how he had watched the faith which was fading down in his soul ageing and strengthening in her eyes. A dim antagonism gathered force within him and darkened his mind as a cloud against her disloyalty: and when it passed, cloudlike, leaving his mind serene and dutiful towards her again, he was made aware dimly and without regret of a first noiseless sundering of their lives.

The university! So he had passed beyond the challenge of the sentries who had stood as guardians of his boyhood and had sought to keep him among them that he might be subject to them and serve their ends. Pride after satisfaction uplifted him like long slow waves. The end he had been born to serve yet did not see had led him to escape by an unseen path and now it beckoned to him once more and a new adventure was about to be opened to him. It seemed to him that he heard notes of fitful music leaping upwards a tone and downwards a diminished fourth, upwards a tone and downwards a major third, like triplebranching flames leaping fitfully, flame after flame, out of a midnight wood. It was an elfin prelude, endless and formless; and, as it grew wilder and faster, the flames leaping out of time, he seemed to hear from under the boughs and grasses wild creatures racing, their feet pattering like rain upon the leaves. Their feet passed in pattering tumult over his mind, the feet of hares and rabbits, the feet of harts and hinds and antelopes, until he heard them no more and remembered only a proud cadence from Newman:

— Whose feet are as the feet of harts and underneath the everlasting arms.

The pride of that dim image brought back to his mind the dignity of the office he had refused. All through his boyhood he had mused upon that which he had so often thought to be his destiny and when the moment had come for him to obey the call he had turned aside, obeying a wayward instinct. Now time lay between: the oils of ordination would never anoint his body. He had refused. Why?

He turned seawards from the road at Dollymount and as he passed on to the thin wooden bridge he felt the planks shaking with the tr mp of heavily shod feet. A squad of christian brothers was on its way back from the Bull and had begun to pass, two by two, across the bridge. Soon

65

the whole bridge was trembling and resounding. The uncouth faces passed him two by two, stained yellow or red or livid by the sea, and, as he strove to look at them with ease and indifference, a faint stain of personal shame and commiseration rose to his own face. Angry with himself he tried to hide his face from their eyes by gazing down sideways into the shallow swirling water under the bridge but he still saw a reflection therein of their topheavy silk hats, and humble tapelike collars and loosely hanging clerical clothes.

— Brother Hickey.

Brother Quaid.

Brother MacArdle.

Brother Keogh. —

Their piety would be like their names, like their faces, like their clothes; and it was idle for him to tell himself that their humble and contrite hearts, it might be, paid a far richer tribute of devotion than his had ever been, a gift tenfold more acceptable than his elaborate adoration. It was idle for him to move himself to be generous towards them, to tell himself that if he ever came to their gates, stripped of his pride, beaten and in beggar's weeds, that they would be generous towards him, loving him as themselves. Idle and embittering, finally, to argue, against his own dispassionate certitude, that the commandment of love bade us not to love our neighbour as ourselves with the same amount and intensity of love but to love him as ourselves with the same kind of love.

He drew forth a phrase from his treasure and spoke it softly to himself:
— A day of dappled seaborne clouds.

The phrase and the day and the scene harmonized in a chord. Words. Was it their colours? He allowed them to glow and fade, hue after hue: sunrise gold, the russet and green of apple orchards, azure of waves, the greyfringed fleece of clouds. No, it was not their colours: it was the poise and balance of the period itself. Did he then love the rhythmic rise and fall of words better than their associations of legend and colour? Or was it that, being as weak of sight as he was shy of mind, he drew less pleasure from the reflection of the glowing sensible world through the prism of a language manycoloured and richly storied than from the contemplation of an inner world of individual emotions mirrored perfectly in a lucid supple periodic prose?

He passed from the trembling bridge on to firm land again. At that instant, as it seemed to him, the air was chilled and, looking askance towards the water, he saw a flying squall darkening and crisping suddenly the tide. A faint click at his heart, a faint throb in his throat told him once more of how his flesh dreaded the cold infrahuman odour of the sea; yet he did not strike across the downs on his left but held straight on along the spine of rocks that pointed against the river's mouth.

A veiled sunlight lit up faintly the grey sheet of water where the river was embayed. In the distance along the course of the slowflowing Liffey slender masts flecked the sky and, more distant still, the dim fabric of the city lay prone in haze. Like a scene on some vague arras, old as man's weariness, the image of the seventh city of christendom was visible to him across the timeless air, no older nor more weary nor less patient of subjection than in the days of the thingmote.

Disheartened, he raised his eyes towards the slowdrifting clouds, dappled and seaborne. They were voyaging across the deserts of the sky, a host of nomads on the march, voyaging high over Ireland, westward bound. The Europe they had come from lay out there beyond the Irish Sea, Europe of strange tongues and valleyed and woodbegirt and cita-delled and of entrenched and marshalled races. He heard a confused music within him as of memories and names which he was almost conscious of but could not capture even for an instant; then the music seemed to recede, to recede, to recede; and from each receding trail of nebulous music there fell always one longdrawn calling note, piercing like a star the dusk of silence. Again! Again! Again! A voice from beyond the world was calling.

— Hello, Stephanos!

— Here comes The Dedalus!

— Ao! . . . Eh, give it over, Dwyer, I'm telling you or I'll give you a stuff in the kisser for yourself . . . Ao!

— Good man, Towser! Duck him!

— Come along, Dedalus! Bous Stephanoumenos! Bous Stephaneforos!

— Duck him! Guzzle him now, Towser!

— Help! Help! . . . Ao!

He recognized their speech collectively before he distinguished their faces. The mere sight of that medley of wet nakedness chilled him to the bone. Their bodies, corpsewhite or suffused with a pallid golden light or rawly tanned by the suns, gleamed with the wet of the sea. Their diving-stone, poised on its rude supports and rocking under their plunges, and the roughhewn stones of the sloping breakwater over which they scrambled in their horseplay, gleamed with cold wet lustre. The towels with which they smacked their bodies were heavy with cold seawater: and drenched with cold brine was their matted hair.

He stood still in deference to their calls and parried their banter with easy words. How characterless they looked: Shuley without his deep unbuttoned collar, Ennis without his scarlet belt with the snaky clasp, and Connolly without his Norfolk coat with the flapless sidepockets! It was a pain to see them and a swordlike pain to see the signs of adolescence that made repellent their pitiable nakedness. Perhaps they had taken refuge in number and noise from the secret dread in their souls. But he, apart from them and in silence, remembered in what dread he stood of the mystery of his own body.

— Stephanos Dedalos! Bous Stephanoumenos! Bous Stephaneforos!

Their banter was not new to him and now it flattered his mild proud sovereignty. Now, as never before, his strange name seemed to him a prophecy. So timeless seemed the grey warm air, so fluid and impersonal his own mood, that all ages were as one to him. A moment before the ghost of the ancient kingdom of the Danes had looked forth through the vesture of the hazewrapped city. Now, at the name of the fabulous artificer, he seemed to hear the noise of dim waves and to see a winged form flying above the waves and slowly climbing the air. What did it mean? Was it a quaint device opening a page of some medieval book of prophecies and symbols, a hawklike man flying sunwards above the sea, a prophecy of the end he had been born to serve and had been following through the mists of childhood and boyhood, a symbol of the artist forging anew in his workshop out of the sluggish matter of the earth a new soaring impalpable imperishable being?

His heart trembled; his breath came faster and a wild spirit passed over his limbs as though he were soaring sunwards. His heart trembled in an ecstasy of fear and his soul was in flight. His soul was soaring in an air beyond the world and the body he knew was purified in a breath and delivered of incertitude and made radiant and commingled with the element of the spirit. An ecstasy of flight made radiant his eyes and wild his breath and tremulous and wild and radiant his windswept limbs.

— One! Two! . . . Look out!

— O, Cripes, I'm drownded!

— One! Two! Three and away!

— The next! The next!

— One! . . . Uk!

— Stephaneforos!

His throat ached with a desire to cry aloud, the cry of a hawk or eagle on high, to cry piercingly of his deliverance to the winds. This was the call of life to his soul not the dull gross voice of the world of duties and despair, not the inhuman voice that had called him to the pale service of the altar. An instant of wild flight had delivered him and the cry of triumph which his lips withheld cleft his brain.

— Stephaneforos!

What were they now but the cerements shaken from the body of death—the fear he had walked in night and day, the incertitude that had ringed him round, the shame that had abased him within and without—cerements, the linens of the grave?

His soul had arisen from the grave of boyhood, spurning her graveclothes. Yes! Yes! Yes! He would create proudly out of the freedom and power of his soul, as the great artificer whose name he bore, a living thing, new and soaring and beautiful, impalpable, imperishable.

He started up nervously from the stone block for he could no longer quench the flame in his blood. He felt his cheeks aflame and his throat throbbing with song. There was a lust of wandering in his feet that burned to set out for the ends of the earth. On! On! his heart seemed to cry. Evening would deepen above the sea, night fall upon the plains, dawn glimmer before the wanderer and show him strange fields and hills and faces. Where?

He looked northward towards Howth. The sea had fallen below the line of seawrack on the shallow side of the breakwater and already the tide was running out fast along the foreshore. Already one long oval bank of sand lay warm and dry amid the wavelets. Here and there warm isles of sand gleamed above the shallow tides and about the isles and around the long bank and amid the shallow currents of the beach were lightclad figures, wading and delving.

In a few moments he was barefoot, his stockings folded in his pockets, and his canvas shoes dangling by their knotted laces over his shoulders and, picking a pointed salteaten stick out of the jetsam among the rocks, he clambered down the slope of the breakwater.

There was a long rivulet in the strand and, as he waded slowly up its course, he wondered at the endless drift of seaweed. Emerald and black and russet and olive, it moved beneath the current, swaying and turning. The water of the rivulet was dark with endless drift and mirrored the highdrifting clouds. The clouds were drifting above him silently and silently the seatangle was drifting below him; and the grey warm air was still; and a new wild life was singing in his veins.

Where was his boyhood now? Where was the soul that had hung back from her destiny, to brood alone upon the shame of her wounds and in her house of squalor and subterfuge to queen it in faded cerements and in wreaths that withered at the touch? Or where was he?

He was alone. He was unheeded, happy, and near to the wild heart of life. He was alone and young and wilful and wildhearted, alone amidst a waste of wild air and brackish waters and the seaharvest of shells and tangle and veiled grey sunlight and gayclad lightclad figures of children and girls and voices childish and girlish in the air.

A girl stood before him in midstream, alone and still, gazing out to sea. She seemed like one whom magic had changed into the likeness of a strange and beautiful seabird. Her long slender bare legs were delicate as a crane's and pure save where an emerald trail of seaweed had fashioned itself as a sign upon the flesh. Her thighs, fuller and softhued as ivory, were bared almost to the hips where the white fringes of her drawers were like feathering of soft white down. Her slateblue skirts were kilted boldly about her waist and dovetailed behind her. Her bosom was as a bird's, soft and slight, slight and soft as the breast of some darkplumaged dove. But her long fair hair was girlish; and girlish, and touched with the wonder of mortal beauty, her face.

She was alone and still, gazing out to sea; and when she felt his presence and the worship of his eyes her eyes turned to him in quiet sufferance of his gaze, without shame or wantonness. Long, long she suffered his gaze and then quietly withdrew her eyes from his and bent them towards the stream, gently stirring the water with her foot hither and thither. The first faint noise of gently moving water broke the silence, low and faint and whispering, faint as the bells of sleep; hither and thither; hither and thither; and a faint flame trembled on her cheek.

— Heavenly God! cried Stephen's soul, in an outburst of profane joy.

He turned away from her suddenly and set off across the strand. His cheeks were aflame; his body was aglow; his limbs were trembling. On and on and on and on he strode, far out over the sands, singing wildly to the sea, crying to greet the advent of the life that had cried to him.

Her image had passed into his soul for ever and no word had broken the holy silence of his ecstasy. Her eyes had called him and his soul had leaped at the call. To live, to err, to fall, to triumph, to recreate life out of life! A wild angel had appeared to him, the angel of mortal youth and beauty, an envoy from the fair courts of life, to throw open before him in an instant of ecstasy the gates of all the ways of error and glory. On and on and on and on!

He halted suddenly and heard his heart in the silence. How far had he walked? What hour was it?

There was no human figure near him nor any sound borne to him over the air. But the tide was near the turn and already the day was on the wane. He turned landwards and ran towards the shore and, running up the sloping beach, reckless of the sharp shingle, found a sandy nook amid a ring of tufted sandknolls and lay down there that the peace and silence of the evening might still the riot of his blood.

He felt above him the vast indifferent dome and the calm processes of the heavenly bodies; and the earth beneath him, the earth that had borne him, had taken him to her breast.

He closed his eyes in the languor of sleep. His eyelids trembled as if they felt the vast cyclic movement of the earth and her watchers, trembled as if they felt the strange light of some new world. His soul was swooning into some new world, fantastic, dim, uncertain as under sea, traversed by cloudy shapes and beings. A world, a glimmer, or a flower? Glimmering and trembling, trembling and unfolding, a breaking light, an opening flower, it spread in endless succession to itself, breaking in full crimson and unfolding and fading to palest rose, leaf by leaf and wave of light by wave of light, flooding all the heavens with its soft flashes, every flush deeper than other.

Evening had fallen when he woke and the sand and arid grasses of his bed glowed no longer. He rose slowly and, recalling the rapture of his sleep, sighed at its joy.

He climbed at the crest of the sandhill and gazed about him. Evening had fallen. A rim of the young moon cleft the pale waste of skyline, the rim of a silver hoop embedded in grey sand; and the tide was flowing in fast to the land with a low whisper of her waves, islanding a few last figures in distant pools.

Aldous Huxley

Aldous Huxley (1894–1963) was educated at Eton and Balliol. He was the grandson of T. H. Huxley and brother of Sir Julian Huxley. In 1937 he went to live in California.

His forty books—the first was *Limbo*, a collection of stories, published in 1920 and the last *Literature and Science* published in 1963—include fiction, travel, philosophy, collections of essays and biography.

His first novels, *Crome Yellow* (1921), *Antic Hay* (1923), *Those Barren Leaves* (1925), *Point Counter Point* (1928) are full of wit, learning, speculation, of charm. In the 'twenties when the contemporary novel meant Bennett, Galsworthy, Wells and Walpole, Aldous Huxley made a dazzling impact. As Wells had been twenty years earlier, Huxley was a popularizer of 'advanced' ideas, though his emphasis was on art rather than science. It seemed that all art, all literature and philosophy were at his disposal for comment and speculation. He was excitingly frank about sex; *Antic Hay* was banned by some libraries though to-day the 'obscene' passages would hardly arouse comment if published in a school magazine.

Brave New World (1932) marks the end of Huxley's first phase as a novelist. He became increasingly concerned with social and ethical speculation. In novels like *Eyeless in Gaza* (1936) and *After Many a Summer* (1939) the characters are less convincing as human beings; fiction was now a vehicle for philosophical discussion, most of it very stimulating indeed.

Crome Yellow   **The Civilized Attitude**

Mary and other guests are staying at Crome, the ancestral home of Henry and Priscilla Wimbush. Anne is their niece. The action of the novel takes place on a few summer days between the end of the war in 1918, and 1921 when the book was published.

At Crome all the beds were ancient hereditary pieces of furniture. Huge beds, like four-masted ships, with furled sails of shining coloured stuff. Beds carved and inlaid, beds painted and gilded. Beds of walnut and oak, of rare exotic woods. Beds of every date and fashion from the time of Sir Ferdinando, who built the house, to the time of his namesake in the late eighteenth century, the last of the family, but all of them grandiose, magnificent.

The finest of all was now Anne's bed. Sir Julius, son to Sir Ferdinando, had had it made in Venice against his wife's first lying-in. Early *seicento* Venice had expended all its extravagant art in the making of it. The body of the bed was like a great square sarcophagus. Clustering roses were carved in high relief on its wooden panels, and luscious *putti* wallowed among the roses. On the black groundwork of the panels the carved reliefs were gilded and burnished. The golden roses twined in spirals up the four pillar-like posts, and cherubs, seated at the top of each column, supported a wooden canopy fretted with the same carved flowers.

Anne was reading in bed. Two candles stood on the little table beside her. In their rich light her face, her bare arm and shoulder took on warm hues and a sort of peach-like quality of surface. Here and there in the canopy above her carved golden petals shone brightly among profound shadows, and the soft light, falling on the sculptured panel of the bed, broke restlessly among the intricate roses, lingered in a broad caress on the blown cheeks, the dimpled bellies, the tight, absurd little posteriors of the sprawling *putti*.

There was a discreet tap at the door. She looked up. 'Come in, come in.' A face, round and childish within its sleek bell of golden hair, peered round the opening door. More childish-looking still, a suit of mauve pyjamas made its entrance.

It was Mary. 'I thought I'd just look in for a moment to say good-night,' she said, and sat down on the edge of the bed.

Anne closed her book. 'That was very sweet of you.'

'What are you reading?' She looked at the book. 'Rather second-rate, isn't it?' The tone in which Mary pronounced the word 'second-rate' implied an almost infinite denigration. She was accustomed in London to associate only with first-rate people who liked first-rate things, and she knew that there were very, very few first-rate things in the world, and that those were mostly French.

'Well, I'm afraid I like it,' said Anne. There was nothing more to be said. The silence that followed was a rather uncomfortable one. Mary fiddled uneasily with the bottom button of her pyjama jacket. Leaning back on her mound of heaped-up pillows, Anne waited and wondered what was coming.

'I'm so awfully afraid of repressions,' said Mary at last, bursting suddenly and surprisingly into speech. She pronounced the words on the tail-end of an expiring breath, and had to gasp for new air almost before the phrase was finished.

'What's there to be depressed about?'

'I said repressions, not depressions.'

'Oh, repressions; I see,' said Anne. 'But repressions of what?'

Mary had to explain. 'The natural instincts of sex . . .' she began didactically. But Anne cut her short.

'Yes, yes. Perfectly. I understand. Repressions; old maids and all the rest. But what about them?'

'That's just it,' said Mary. 'I'm afraid of them. It's always dangerous to repress one's instincts. I'm beginning to detect in myself symptoms like the ones you read of in the books. I constantly dream that I'm falling down wells; and sometimes I even dream that I'm climbing up ladders. It's most disquieting. The symptoms are only too clear.'

'Are they?'

'One may become a nymphomaniac if one's not careful. You've no idea how serious these repressions are if you don't get rid of them in time.'

'It sounds too awful,' said Anne. 'But I don't see that I can do anything to help you.'

'I thought I'd just like to talk it over with you.'

'Why, of course; I'm only too happy, Mary darling.'

Mary coughed and drew a deep breath. 'I presume,' she began sententiously, 'I presume we may take for granted that an intelligent young woman of twenty-three who has lived in civilized society in the twentieth century has no prejudices.'

'Well, I confess I still have a few.'

'But not about repressions.'

'No, not many about repressions; that's true.'

'Or, rather, about getting rid of repressions.'

'Exactly.'

'So much for our fundamental postulate,' said Mary. Solemnity was expressed in every feature of her round young face, radiated from her large blue eyes. 'We come next to the desirability of possessing experience. I hope we are agreed that knowledge is desirable and that ignorance is undesirable.'

Obedient as one of those complaisant disciples from whom Socrates could get whatever answer he chose, Anne gave her assent to this proposition.

'And we are equally agreed, I hope, that marriage is what it is.'

'It is.'

'Good!' said Mary. 'And repressions being what they are . . .'

'Exactly.'

'There would therefore seem to be only one conclusion.'

'But I knew that,' Anne exclaimed, 'before you began.'

'Yes, but now it's been proved,' said Mary. 'One must do things logically. The question is now . . .'

'But where does the question come in? You've reached your only possible conclusion—logically, which is more than I could have done. All that remains is to impart the information to someone you like—someone you like really rather a lot, someone you're in love with, if I may express myself so baldly.'

'But that's just where the question comes in,' Mary exclaimed. 'I'm not in love with anybody.'

'Then if I were you, I should wait till you are.'

'But I can't go on dreaming night after night that I'm falling down a well. It's too dangerous.'

'Well, if it really is *too* dangerous, then of course you must do something about it; you must find somebody else.'

'But who?' A thoughtful frown puckered Mary's brow. 'It must be somebody intelligent, somebody with intellectual interests that I can share. And it must be somebody with a proper respect for women, somebody who's prepared to talk seriously about his work and his ideas and about my work and my ideas. It isn't, as you see, at all easy to find the right person.'

'Well,' said Anne, 'there are three unattached and intelligent men in the house at the present time. There's Mr Scogan, to begin with; but perhaps he's rather too much of a genuine antique. And there are Gombauld and Denis. Shall we say that the choice is limited to the last two?'

Mary nodded. 'I think we had better,' she said, and then hesitated, with a certain air of embarrasssment.

'What is it?'

'I was wondering,' said Mary, with a gasp, 'whether they really were unattached. I thought that perhaps you might . . . you might . . .'

'It was very nice of you to think of me, Mary darling,' said Anne, smiling the tight cat's smile. 'But as far as I'm concerned, they are both entirely unattached.'

'I'm very glad of that,' said Mary, looking relieved. 'We are now confronted with the question: Which of the two?'

'I can give no advice. It's a matter for your taste.'

'It's not a matter of my taste,' Mary pronounced, 'but of their merits. We must weigh them and consider them carefully and dispassionately.'

'You must do the weighing yourself,' said Anne; there was still the trace of a smile at the corners of her mouth and round the half-closed eyes. 'I won't run the risk of advising you wrongly.'

'Gombauld has more talent,' Mary began, 'but he is less civilized than Denis.' Mary's pronunciation of 'civilized' gave the word a special and additional significance. She uttered it meticulously, in the very front of her mouth, hissing delicately on the opening sibilant. So few people were civilized, and they, like the first-rate works of art, were mostly French. 'Civilization is most important, don't you think?'

Anne held up her hand. 'I won't advise,' she said. 'You must make the decision.'

'Gombauld's family,' Mary went on reflectively, 'comes from Marseilles. Rather a dangerous heredity, when one thinks of the Latin attitude towards women. But then, I sometimes wonder whether Denis is altogether serious-minded, whether he isn't rather a dilettante. It's very difficult. What do you think?'

'I'm not listening,' said Anne. 'I refuse to take any responsibility.'

Mary sighed. 'Well,' she said, 'I think I had better go to bed and think about it.'

'Carefully and dispassionately,' said Anne.

At the door, Mary turned round. 'Good-night,' she said, and wondered as she said the words why Anne was smiling in that curious way. It was probably nothing, she reflected. Anne often smiled for no apparent reason; it was probably just a habit. 'I hope I shan't dream of falling down

wells again to night,' she added.
'Ladders are worse,' said Anne.
Mary nodded. 'Yes, ladders are much graver.'

Brave New World **Preparation for Life**

A description of a possible world six centuries in the future. Perhaps the most remarkable feature of this world is the thoroughness with which its citizens are conditioned. 'That is the secret of happiness and virtue—liking what you've got to do. All conditioning aims at that: making people like their inescapable social destiny,' explains the Director of the London Hatchery and Conditioning Centre. Mustapha Mond, the World Controller, claims that 'People are happy; they get what they want, and they never want what they can't get.' He points out that 'an Alpha-decanted, Alpha-conditioned man would go mad if he had to do Epsilon Semi-Moron work.'

The novel is a satire, of course; but not everyone would dismiss the assumptions of the New World without a second thought. 'In the moon,' says Cavor in Wells's The First Men in the Moon, 'every citizen knows his place. He is born to that place and the elaborate discipline of training and education and surgery he undergoes fits him at last so completely to it that he has neither ideas nor organs for any purpose beyond it . . . it haunts me still, although, of course, it is really in the end a far more humane proceeding than our earthly method of leaving children to grow into human beings, and then making machines of them.' Wells, an Alpha man, had left school to work twelve to fourteen hours a day in a draper's shop.

Brave New World is rich in suggestion about our society. A group of students is being shown round the Central London Hatchery and Conditioning Centre, by the Director himself.

Mr Foster was left in the Decanting Room. The D.H.C. and his students stepped into the nearest lift and were carried up to the fifth floor.

INFANT NURSERIES. NEO-PAVLOVIAN CONDITIONING ROOMS, announced the notice board.

The Director opened a door. They were in a large bare room, very bright and sunny; for the whole of the southern wall was a single window. Half a dozen nurses, trousered and jacketed in the regulation white viscose-linen uniform, their hair aseptically hidden under white caps, were engaged in setting out bowls of roses in a long row across the floor. Big bowls, packed tight with blossom. Thousands of petals, ripe-blown and silkily smooth, like the cheeks of innumerable little cherubs, but of cherubs, in that bright light, not exclusively pink and Aryan, but also luminously Chinese, also Mexican, also apoplectic with too much blowing of celestial trumpets, also pale as death, pale with the posthumous whiteness of marble.

The nurses stiffened to attention as the D.H.C. came in.

'Set out the books,' he said curtly.

In silence the nurses obeyed his command. Between the rose bowls the books were duly set out—a row of nursery quartos opened invitingly each at some gaily coloured image of beast or fish or bird.

'Now bring in the children.'

They hurried out of the room and returned in a minute or two, each pushing a kind of tall dumb-waiter laden, on all its four wire-netted shelves, with eight-month old babies, all exactly alike (a Bokanovsky Group, it was evident) and all (since their caste was Delta) dressed in khaki.

'Put them down on the floor.'

The infants were unloaded.

'Now turn them so that they can see the flowers and books.'

Turned, the babies at once fell silent, then began to crawl towards those clusters of sleek colours, those shapes so gay and brilliant on the white pages. As they approached, the sun came out of a momentary eclipse behind a cloud. The roses flamed up as though with a sudden passion from within; a new and profound significance seemed to suffuse the shining pages of the books. From the ranks of the crawling babies came little squeals of excitement, gurgles and twitterings of pleasure.

The Director rubbed his hands. 'Excellent!' he said. 'It might almost have been done on purpose.'

The swiftest crawlers were already at their goal. Small hands reached out uncertainly, touched, grasped, unpetaling the transfigured roses, crumpling the illuminated pages of the books. The Director waited until all were happily busy. Then, 'Watch carefully,' he said. And, lifting his hand, he gave the signal.

The Head Nurse, who was standing by a switchboard at the other end of the room, pressed down a little lever.

There was a violent explosion. Shriller and ever shriller, a siren shrieked. Alarm bells maddeningly sounded.

The children started, screamed; their faces were distorted with terror. 'And now,' the Director shouted (for the noise was deafening), 'now we proceed to rub in the lesson with a mild electric shock.'

He waved his hand again, and the Head Nurse pressed a second lever. The screaming of the babies suddenly changed its tone. There was something desperate, almost insane, about the sharp spasmodic yelps to which they now gave utterance. Their little bodies twitched and stiffened; their limbs moved jerkily as if to the tug of unseen wires.

'We can electrify that whole strip of floor,' bawled the Director in explanation. 'But that's enough,' he signalled to the nurse.

The explosions ceased, the bells stopped ringing, the shriek of the siren died down from tone to tone into silence. The stiffly twitching bodies relaxed, and what had become the sob and yelp of infant maniacs broadened out once more into a normal howl of ordinary terror.

'Offer them the flowers and the books again.'

The nurses obeyed; but at the approach of the roses, at the mere sight of those gaily-coloured images of pussy and cock-a-doodle-doo and baa-baa black sheep, the infants shrank away in horror; the volume of their howling suddenly increased.

'Observe,' said the Director triumphantly, 'observe.'

Books and loud noises, flowers and electric shocks—already in the infant mind these couples were compromisingly linked; and after two hundred repetitions of the same or a similar lesson would be wedded indissolubly. What man has joined, nature is powerless to put asunder.

'They'll grow up with what the psychologists used to call an "instinctive" hatred of books and flowers. Reflexes unalterably conditioned. They'll be safe from books and botany all their lives.' The Director turned to his nurses. 'Take them away again.'

Still yelling, the khaki babies were loaded on to their dumb-waiters and wheeled out, leaving behind them the smell of sour milk and a most welcome silence.

Fifty yards of tiptoeing brought them to a door which the Director cautiously opened. They stepped over the threshold into the twilight of a shuttered dormitory. Eighty cots stood in a row against the wall. There was a sound of light regular breathing and a continuous murmur, as of very faint voices remotely whispering.

A nurse rose as they entered and came to attention before the Director. 'What's the lesson this afternoon?' he asked.

'We had Elementary Sex for the first forty minutes,' she answered. 'But now it's switched over to Elementary Class Consciousness.'

The Director walked slowly down the long line of cots. Rosy and relaxed with sleep, eighty little boys and girls lay softly breathing. There was a whisper under every pillow. The D.H.C. halted and, bending over one of the little beds, listened attentively.

'Elementary Class Consciousness, did you say? Let's have it repeated a little louder by the trumpet.'

At the end of the room a loud-speaker projected from the wall. The Director walked up to it and pressed a switch.

'. . . all wear green,' said a soft but very distinct voice, beginning in the middle of a sentence, 'and Delta children wear khaki. Oh no, I don't want to play with Delta children. And Epsilons are still worse. They're too stupid to be able to read or write. Besides, they wear black, which is such a beastly colour. I'm *so* glad I'm a Beta.'

There was a pause; then the voice began again.

'Alpha children wear grey. They work much harder than we do, because they're so frightfully clever. I'm really awfully glad I'm a Beta, because I don't work so hard. And then we are much better than the Gammas and Deltas. Gammas are stupid. They all wear green, and Delta children wear khaki. Oh no, I *don't* want to play with Delta children. And Epsilons are still worse. They're too stupid to be able . . .'

The Director pushed back the switch. The voice was silent. Only its thin ghost continued to mutter from beneath the eighty pillows.

'They'll have that repeated forty or fifty times more before they wake; then again on Thursday, and again on Saturday. A hundred and twenty times three times a week for thirty months. After which they go on to a more advanced lesson.

Roses and electric shocks, the khaki of Deltas and a whiff of asafoetida— wedded indissolubly before the child can speak. But wordless conditioning is crude and wholesale; cannot bring home the finer distinctions, cannot inculcate the more complex courses of behaviour. For that there must be words, but words without reason. In brief, hypnopaedia.

'The greatest moralizing and socializing force of all time.'

The students took it down in their little books. Straight from the horse's mouth.

Once more the Director touched the switch.

'. . . so frightfully clever,' the soft, insinuating indefatigable voice was saying. 'I'm really awfully glad I'm a Beta, because . . .'

Not so much like drops of water, though water, it is true, can wear holes in the hardest granite; rather, drops of liquid sealing-wax, drops that adhere, incrust, incorporate themselves with what they fall on, till finally the rock is all one scarlet blob.

'Till at last the child's mind *is* these suggestions, and the sum of the suggestions *is* the child's mind. And not the child's mind only. The adult's mind too—all his life long. The mind that judges and desires and decides—made up of these suggestions. But all these suggestions are *our* suggestions!' The Director almost shouted in his triumph. 'Suggestions from the State.' He banged the nearest table. 'It therefore follows . . .'

A noise made him turn round.

'Oh, Ford!' he said in another tone. 'I've gone and woken the children.'

F

E M Forster

Edward Morgan Forster was born in London in 1879. He was educated at Tonbridge School and King's College, Cambridge. As a young man he spent a good deal of time on the Continent, particularly in Italy and Germany. Mr Forster has written five novels, the first four between 1905 and 1910; *A Passage to India* was published in 1924.

Mr Forster is not primarily a story-teller. 'Yes—oh dear yes, the novel tells a story . . . and I wish that it was not so, that it could be something different—melody, or perception of the truth, not this low atavistic form,' he has written. Nor is he concerned to chronicle an epoch or a society, as Arnold Bennett did, for example, by filling his work with representative characters and realistic detail. He is concerned rather to seek, to reveal the truth about a character, a relationship, a situation. For this purpose he may describe action that is symbolic rather than realistic.

Mr Forster is a liberal, an agnostic, an anti-imperialist. Fundamental to his attitude is his belief in the sanctity of human affections. His theme is the difficulty and importance of establishing right relationships. The target of his criticism is 'the undeveloped heart'—in *A Passage to India* the insensitive, conventional public school men who governed India.

A Passage to India An Interrupted Evening with Friends

Dr Aziz was the assistant of Dr Callendar, the Civil Surgeon at Chandrapore. Cyril Fielding was Principal of Government College. The two men were mutually attracted, but their friendship was assaulted by many difficulties, both gross and subtle. They sprang from different races, the one dominant, the other subject. Here Aziz is speaking to Fielding: 'And Aziz in an awful rage danced this way and that, not knowing what to do, and cried: "Down with the English, anyhow. That's certain. Clear out you fellows, double quick, I say. We may hate one another, but we hate you most. If I don't make you go, Ahmed will, Karim will, if it's fifty-five hundred years we shall get rid of you; yes, we shall drive every blasted Englishman into the sea, and then"—he rode against him furiously—"and then," he concluded, half kissing him, "you and I shall be friends." '

Abandoning his bicycle, which fell before a servant could catch it, the young man sprang on to the veranda. He was all animation. 'Hamidullah, Hamidullah! am I late?' he cried.

'Do not apologize,' said his host. 'You are always late.'

'Kindly answer my question. Am I late? Has Mahmoud Ali eaten all the food? If so I go elsewhere. Mr Mahmoud Ali, how are you?'

'Thank you, Dr Aziz, I am dying.'

'Dying before your dinner? Oh, poor Mahmoud Ali!'

'Hamidullah here is actually dead. He passed away just as you rode up on your bike.'

'Yes, that is so,' said the other. 'Imagine us both as addressing you from another and a happier world.'

'Does there happen to be such a thing as a hookah in that happier world of yours?'

'Aziz, don't chatter. We are having a very sad talk.'

The hookah had been packed too tight, as was usual in his friend's house, and bubbled sulkily. He coaxed it. Yielding at last, the tobacco jetted up into his lungs and nostrils, driving out the smoke of burning cow dung that had filled them as he rode through the bazaar. It was delicious. He lay in a trance, sensuous but healthy, through which the talk of the two others did not seem particularly sad—they were discussing as to whether or no it is possible to be friends with an Englishman. Mahmoud Ali argued that it was not, Hamidullah disagreed, but with so many reservations that there was no friction between them. Delicious indeed to lie on the broad veranda with the moon rising in front and the servants preparing dinner behind, and no trouble happening.

'Well, look at my own experience this morning.'

'I only contend that it is possible in England,' replied Hamidullah, who had been to that country long ago, before the big rush, and had received a cordial welcome at Cambridge.

'It is impossible here. Aziz! The red-nosed boy has again insulted me in Court. I do not blame him. He was told that he ought to insult me. Until lately he was quite a nice boy, but the others have got hold of him.'

'Yes, they have no chance here, that is my point. They come out intending to be gentlemen, and are told it will not do. Look at Lesley, look at Blakiston, now it is your red-nosed boy, and Fielding will go next. Why, I remember when Turton came out first. It was in another part of the province. You fellows will not believe me, but I have driven with Turton in his carriage—Turton! Oh yes, we were once quite intimate. He has shown me his stamp collection.'

'He would expect you to steal it now. Turton! But red-nosed boy will be far worse than Turton!'

'I do not think so. They all become exactly the same, not worse, not better. I give any Englishman two years, be he Turton or Burton. It is only the difference of a letter. And I give any Englishwoman six months. All are exactly alike. Do you not agree with me?'

'I do not,' replied Mahmoud Ali, entering into the bitter fun, and feeling both pain and amusement at each word that was uttered. 'For my own part I find such profound differences among our rulers. Red-nose mumbles, Turton talks distinctly, Mrs Turton takes bribes, Mrs Red-nose does not and cannot, because so far there is no Mrs Red-nose.'

'Bribes?'

'Did you not know that when they were lent to Central India over a Canal Scheme, some Rajah or other gave her a sewing machine in solid gold so that the water should run through his state.'

'And does it?'

'No; that is where Mrs Turton is so skilful. When we poor blacks take bribes, we perform what we are bribed to perform, and the law discovers us in consequence. The English take and do nothing. I admire them.'

'We all admire them. Aziz, please pass me the hookah.'

'Oh, not yet—hookah is so jolly now.'

'You are a very selfish boy.' He raised his voice suddenly, and shouted for dinner. Servants shouted back that it was ready. They meant that they wished it was ready, and were so understood, for nobody moved. Then Hamidullah continued, but with changed manner and evident emotion.

'But take my case—the case of young Hugh Bannister. Here is the son of my dear, my dead friends, the Reverend and Mrs Bannister, whose goodness to me in England I shall never forget or describe. They were father and mother to me, I talked to them as I do now. In the vacations their rectory became my home. They entrusted all their children to me— I often carried little Hugh about—I took him up to the Funeral of Queen Victoria, and held him in my arms above the crowd.'

'Queen Victoria was different,' murmured Mahmoud Ali.

'I learn now that this boy is in business as a leather merchant at Cawnpore. Imagine how I long to see him and to pay his fare that this house may be his home. But it is useless. The other Anglo-Indians will have got hold of him long ago. He will probably think that I want something, and I cannot face that from the son of my old friends. Oh, what in this country has gone wrong with everything, Vakil Sahib? I ask you.'

Aziz joined in. 'Why talk about the English? Brrr. . . . ! Why be either friends with the fellows or not friends? Let us shut them out and be jolly. Queen Victoria and Mrs Bannister were the only exceptions, and they're dead.'

'No, no, I do not admit that; I have met others.'

'So have I,' said Mahmoud Ali, unexpectedly veering. 'All ladies are far from alike.' Their mood was changed, and they recalled little kindnesses and courtesies. 'She said "Thank you so much" in the most natural way.' 'She offered me a lozenge when the dust irritated my throat.' Hamidullah could remember more important examples of angelic ministration; but the other, who only knew Anglo-India, had to ransack his memory for scraps, and it was not surprising that he should return to 'But of course all this is exceptional. The exception does not prove the rule. The average woman is like Mrs Turton, and, Aziz, you know what she is.' Aziz did not know, but said he did. He too generalized from his disappointments—it is difficult for members of a subject race to do otherwise. Granted the exceptions, he agreed that all Englishwomen are haughty and venal. The gleam passed from the conversation, whose wintry surface unrolled and expanded interminably.

A servant announced dinner. They ignored him. The elder men had reached their eternal politics; Aziz drifted into the garden. The trees smelt sweet—green-blossomed champak—and scraps of Persian poetry came into his head. Dinner, dinner, dinner . . . but when he returned to the house for it Mahmoud Ali had drifted away in his turn, to speak to his sais. 'Come and see my wife a little then,' said Hamidullah, and they spent twenty minutes behind the purdah. Hamidullah Begum was a distant aunt of Aziz, and the only female relative he had in Chandrapore, and she had much to say to him on this occasion about a family circumcision that had been celebrated with imperfect pomp. It was difficult to get away, because until they had had their dinner she would not begin hers, and consequently prolonged her remarks in case they should suppose she was impatient. Having censured the circumcision, she bethought her of kindred topics, and asked Aziz when he was going to be married.

Respectful but irritated, he answered: 'Once is enough.'

'Yes, he has done his duty,' said Hamidullah. 'Do not tease him so. He carries on his family, two boys and their sister.'

'Aunt, they live most comfortably with my wife's mother, where she was living when she died. I can see them whenever I like. They are very, very small children.'

'And he sends them the whole of his salary and lives like a low-grade clerk, and tells no one the reason. What more do you require him to do?'

But this was not Hamidullah Begum's point, and having courteously changed the conversation for a few moments she returned and made it. She said: 'What is to become of all our daughters if men refuse to marry? They will marry beneath them, or——' And she began the oft-told tale of a lady of imperial descent who could find no husband in the narrow circle where her pride permitted her to mate, and had lived on unwed, her age now thirty, and would die unwed, for no one would have her now. While the tale was in progress, it convinced the two men, the tragedy seemed a slur on the whole community; better polygamy almost, than that a woman should die without the joys God has intended her to receive. Wedlock, motherhood, power in the house—for what else is she born, and how can the man who has denied them to her stand up to face her Creator and his own at the last day? Aziz took his leave saying: 'Perhaps . . . but later . . .'—his invariable reply to such an appeal.

'You mustn't put off what you think right,' said Hamidullah. 'That is why India is in such a plight, because we put off things.' But seeing that his young relative looked worried, he added a few soothing words, and thus wiped out any impression that his wife might have made.

During their absence Mahmoud Ali had gone off in his carriage, leaving a message that he should be back in five minutes, but they were on no account to wait. They sat down to meat with a distant cousin of the house, Mohammed Latif, who lived on Hamidullah's bounty and who occupied the position neither of a servant nor of an equal. He did not speak unless spoken to, and since no one spoke kept unoffended silence. Now and then he belched, in compliment to the richness of the food. A gentle, happy, and dishonest old man; all his life he had never done a stroke of work. So long as some one of his relatives had a house he was sure of a home, and it was unlikely that so large a family would all go bankrupt. His wife led a similar existence some hundreds of miles away— he did not visit her, owing to the expense of the railway ticket. Presently Aziz chaffed him, also the servants, and then began quoting poetry, Persian, Urdu, a little Arabic. His memory was good, and for so young a man he had read largely; the themes he preferred were the decay of Islam and the brevity of love. They listened delighted, for they took the public view of poetry, not the private which obtains in England. It never bored them to hear words, words; they breathed them with the cool night air, never stopping to analyse; the name of the poet, Hafiz, Hali, Iqbal, was sufficient guarantee. India—a hundred Indias—whispered outside beneath the indifferent moon; but for the time India seemed one and their own, and they regained their departed greatness by hearing its departure lamented, they felt young again because reminded that youth must fly. A servant in scarlet interrupted him; he was the chuprassi of the Civil Surgeon, and he handed Aziz a note.

'Old Callendar wants to see me at his bungalow,' he said, not rising. 'He might have the politeness to say why.'

'Some case, I dare say.'

'I dare say not, I dare say nothing. He has found out our dinner hour, that's all, and chooses to interrupt us every time, in order to show his power.'

'On the one hand, he always does this; on the other, it may be a serious case, and you cannot know,' said Hamidullah, considerately paving the way towards obedience. 'Had you not better clean your teeth after pan?'

'If my teeth are to be cleaned, I don't go at all. I am an Indian, it is an Indian habit to take pan. The Civil Surgeon must put up with it. Mohammed Latif, my bike, please.'

The poor relation got up. Slightly immersed in the realms of matter, he laid his hand on the bicycle's saddle, while a servant did the actual wheeling. Between them they took it over a tintack. Aziz held his hands under the ewer, dried them, fitted on his green felt hat, and then with unexpected energy whizzed out of Hamidullah's compound.

'Aziz, Aziz, imprudent boy. . . .' But he was far down the bazaar, riding furiously. He had neither light nor bell, nor had he a brake; but what use are such adjuncts in a land where the cyclist's only hope is to coast from face to face, and just before he collides with each it vanishes?

And the city was fairly empty at this hour. When his tyre went flat he leapt off and shouted for a tonga.

He did not at first find one, and he had also to dispose of his bicycle at a friend's house. He dallied furthermore to clean his teeth. But at last he was rattling towards the civil lines, with a vivid sense of speed. As he entered their arid tidiness, depression suddenly seized him. The roads, named after victorious generals and intersecting at right angles, were symbolic of the net Great Britain had thrown over India. He felt caught in their meshes. When he turned into Major Callendar's compound he could with difficulty restrain himself from getting down from the tonga and approaching the bungalow on foot, and this not because his soul was servile, but because his feelings—the sensitive edges of him—feared a gross snub. There had been a 'case' last year—an Indian gentleman had driven up to an official's house and been turned back by the servants and been told to approach more suitably—only one case among thousands of visits to hundreds of officials, but its fame spread wide. The young man shrank from a repetition of it. He compromised, and stopped the driver just outside the flood of light that fell across the veranda.

The Civil Surgeon was out.

'But the sahib has left me some message?'

The servant returned an indifferent 'No.' Aziz was in despair. It was a servant whom he had forgotten to tip, and he could do nothing now because there were people in the hall. He was convinced that there was a message, and that the man was withholding it out of revenge. While they argued the people came out. Both were ladies. Aziz lifted his hat. The first, who was in evening dress, glanced at the Indian and turned instinctively away.

'Mrs Lesley, it *is* a tonga,' she cried.

'Ours?' inquired the second, also seeing Aziz, and doing likewise.

'Take the gifts the gods provide, anyhow,' she screeched, and both jumped in. 'O Tonga wallah, club, club. Why doesn't the fool go?'

'Go; I will pay you to-morrow,' said Aziz to the driver; and as they went off he called courteously: 'You are most welcome, ladies.' They did not reply, being full of their own affairs.

So it had come, the usual thing—just as Mahmoud Ali said. The inevitable snub—his bow ignored, his carriage taken. It might have been worse, for it comforted him somehow that Mesdames Callendar and Lesley should both be fat and weigh the tonga down behind. Beautiful women would have pained him. He turned to the servant, gave him a couple of rupees, and asked again whether there was a message. The man, now very civil, returned the same answer. Major Callendar had driven away half an hour before.

'Saying nothing?'

He had as a matter of fact said: 'Damn Aziz'—words that the servant understood, but was too polite to repeat. One can tip too much as well as too little; indeed the coin that buys the exact truth has not yet been minted.

'Then I will write him a letter.'

He was offered the use of the house, but was too dignified to enter it. Paper and ink were brought on to the veranda. He began: 'Dear Sir, At your express command I have hastened, as a subordinate should—' and then stopped. 'Tell him I have called, that is sufficient,' he said, tearing the protest up. 'Here is my card. Call me a tonga.'

'Huzoor, all are at the club.'

'Then telephone for one down to the railway station.' And since the man hastened to do this he said: 'Enough, enough, I prefer to walk.' He commandeered a match and lit a cigarette. These attentions, though purchased, soothed him. They would last as long as he had rupees, which is something. But to shake the dust of Anglo-India off his feet! To escape from the net and be back among manners and gestures that he knew! He began a walk, an unwonted exercise.

He was an athletic little man, daintily put together, but really very strong. Nevertheless walking fatigued him, as it fatigues every one in India except the new-comer. There is something hostile in that soil. It either yields, and the foot sinks into a depression, or else it is unexpectedly rigid and sharp, pressing stones or crystals against the tread. A series of these little surprises exhausts; and he was wearing pumps, a poor preparation for any country. At the edge of the civil station he turned into a mosque to rest.

Rosamond Lehmann Miss Lehmann was born in Buckinghamshire and educated privately and at Girton College, Cambridge. Her first novel, *Dusty Answer*, published in 1927, was followed by *A Note of Music* in 1930 and *Invitation to the Waltz* in 1932. *The Echoing Grove* appeared in 1953.

Her subject is the life of the intelligent and sensitive woman in our society; her books tell us what it feels like to be a woman.

Invitation to the Waltz **Walking Home**

The whole action of the book takes place on three days in 1920: on Olivia Curtis's seventeenth birthday, the day of her first dance and the day after it. Olivia has received the invitation to the dance. For her birthday her mother has given her a length of red silk. Olivia has just taken it to Miss Robinson, the dressmaker, and is now walking home.

She took the field path that ran up to the green, then down again past the farm to the foot of the garden. From the top of the incline she looked down and saw the village sitting in the faint sun. Smoke went straight up from cottage chimneys, and the women were hanging out their washing. Patches of pink and blue glowed among white patches. One line had a yellow striped apron and one a scarlet petticoat. There was something about the look of the washing and the fences and the arrangements of roofs behind—some thatched, some tiled with old-gold, lichen-covered tiles, all steaming and silvered with pale light—something that made her wish to record it, keep it somehow. It was the beginning of the mood that led to wanting to write poetry. Veils of illusion seemed to float over the familiar scene, half-hiding, half-revealing it under an eternal aspect. It looked like the picture of the village, not like itself.

There in the distance was Mrs Wells-Straker, widow of widows, flowing, streaming towards the church in all her *crêpe*. Was it some Saint's Day, thanksgiving, penance, or commemoration known only to herself and the curate? Or perhaps a private communing with the late Mr Wells-Straker. . . . For his memorial tablet was the pivot of her life; and beneath it she sat, or with loud creaks and rustles knelt, herself a monument, a Stygian effigy, for some part of every day. Mr Smedley must find her fervour and regularity a great encouragement. Why then, did he wear that distant patient look, as of suffering concealed, when he saw her waiting for him in the churchyard after service?

Olivia broke into an imitative jog-trot, then checked herself. It was her best imitation, but she oughtn't to do it. Mrs Wells-Straker was so very kind; and if she met one would gently call Good morning, dear; and when she had asked after Mother, Father, and little brother, would say with loving sympathy: 'And so you'll be losing your dear sister before long. You'll miss her sadly, sadly, I'm afraid. Never mind, dear. Mother could never do without both her dear girls. Your turn will come, dear, all in good time.' And her voice would caress, console, approve; make one feel good for staying at home and bearing the absence of Kate.

Darling Kate—but I don't mind losing her at all—not at all. I don't want to go with her to Paris. I want to do something absolutely different, or perhaps nothing at all; just stay where I am, in my home, and absorb each hour, each day, and be alone; and read and think; and walk about the garden in the night; and wait, wait . . .

Oh dear! There was Major Skinner crossing the cricket pitch towards her, with two retrievers and a spaniel. She hastened her pace. But:

'Hullo, hullo, hullo!' he shouted from some way off, waving his pipe. There was nothing to do but stop, and hope her blush would arrive and subside before he caught up with her. 'Where are you off to, eh? What about that lesson? When are we going to have that? Here am I, waiting every day, always at your service. . . .'

'Oh, thank you, Major Skinner. . . .'

She despaired, was dumb. For some time ago, meeting her near the links, Major Skinner had very kindly offered to teach her to play golf; and ever since she had had to avoid him or try to make excuses. Broad-minded in many ways though Mother was, for some reason she drew the line at golf with Major Skinner; and had been quite disproportionally annoyed when Olivia came home and announced the glad news.

'Well, what about today, what about today? No day like today. Jolly weather. You come along to the links this afternoon and we'll have a round.'

'I'm awfully afraid I can't today.'

'Oh, you can't today. Well, tomorrow then.'

'And tomorrow's Girl Guides.'

'Oh, Girl Guides, is it? What a busy little lady you are, aren't you? Always got something on. That's the spirit. Well, I tell you what: you give me a ring when you're free—see? You give me a ring.'

He was always hopeful, patient under disappointment. He looked her over ruminatively, lustful but gentlemanly, out of small blue blood-shot eyes.

'How's yer sister?'

'She's very well, thank you.'

'Hmm. Give her my salaams. Give her my salaams. And tell her—hmm. And yer father, how's yer father? What's he think of this Irish business? You ask him from me. Tell him I'll come along and have a chat with him one of these days.'

'Yes, rather, I'll tell him.'

He sent this message every time; but she had given up delivering it. It was somewhat oddly received at home; and anyway he never came. He didn't ever send messages to Mother.

She bent to pat a retriever.

'Fond of dogs? Nice brutes. You ought to have a dog, you and Miss Christabel.' He always called Kate Christabel. Perhaps, they thought, she reminded him of someone of that name whom he had once loved; or perhaps he thought it suited her. Or perhaps he just got muddled. He hadn't a very good memory. 'Tell you what: next time Leila here has puppies you shall have one. I'll let you know, and you can come along, both of you, and have first pick.'

'Oh, *thank* you. It *would* be lovely.'

How kind he was. Oh dear! One must just pray Leila wouldn't have any more puppies: for it wouldn't be allowed, it would certainly not be allowed; and it would be so terribly awkward.

'Why don't you and yer sister look in on my wife? Any afternoon. She'd be glad to see you, y'know. It's a bit lonely for her down here—after what she's been used to—in India, y'know—though of course she has her pals down from town . . . bridge . . . D'you play bridge?'

'I'm afraid not.'

'Ah, you ought to play bridge. It's a fine game. A game of skill, y'know. Got to use yer brains. There's an article you're not short of, I'll be bound. Eh? You drop in for a cup of tea one afternoon and get her to give you a lesson.'

'I'd love to.'

Shame, despair again. Even though Dad lifted his hat with particular courtesy when he met Mrs Skinner in the road, even though he referred to her in a light, winking sort of way as that glorious creature, Mrs Skinner was absolutely taboo. For she had a past: twice married, twice divorced; literally dozens of co-respondents; cause of at least one suicide among Indian army subalterns; and now, though long since withdrawn from the fray into the obscure and indigent haven afforded by Major Skinner and there dwelling blamelessly—even, it appeared, devotedly—somehow, what with so much sherry-coloured hair, white powder, vermilion lipstick, what with being childless (after so many opportunities), smoking in the village street, wearing such huge hats, such high heels—somehow she had not contrived to become at all respectable. Or perhaps it was chiefly her voice, so ravishingly rich and husky, tender as ripe fruit, mellowed by years of gin and tobacco; or her smile, so surprisingly sweet, generous, inviting, breaking in her face like the undying flame of a beauty almost swallowed up now in billowing fat.

Anyway, it was being truthful to say one would love to go. She and Kate were united in their desire to make friends with Mrs Skinner. Not that they could altogether condone the lipstick, but one must be tolerant. Probably she didn't realize in her dark little Tudor cottage—re-christened CHOTA-GHURR by Major Skinner—what a terrible lot she put on. Then the house was so thrilling—quite unlike anyone else's—full of luscious green, blue, and purple cushions richly trimmed with gold braid, and brilliant shawls and pieces of embroidery, and huge signed photographs, and heavy perfumes, and cigarette smoke: very exotic, as Kate said. She was unconventional, that was all—awfully nice; they longed to go to tea with her. But it was no good: and Mrs Skinner knew it. That was clear from her manner when they met in the street. Each time she seemed to shrug her shoulders; though all she did was to greet one in passing with a friendly but ironic smile, a tiny shake of the head at once humorous and dignified; and straight on she went, leaving in her wake more than a whiff of camelia: something impalpable that seemed to surround her always, to trail after her, making hunger: a promise of comfort; as if, heaping the fire, drawing curtains, lighting soft lamps, she were saying in that voice of hers: Yes. Yes. How foolish. What a pity. Never mind. Drink. Eat. Rest. I know. I know . . . and so smoothing out furrows of thought, brushing away anxious questions.

Suddenly Olivia felt inclined to smile warmly, lingeringly at Major Skinner. She did so. She didn't care. He was a dear. She was attracted by his human, his male quality—simple, sensual, kindly, pathetic. She was sorry for him, because all his offering was nothing but asking—tentative, shamefaced, pretty sure it was no go, but never altogether daunted. Poor old fumbling suppliant: he was getting old, he didn't have much fun. The nice, the fresh young girls avoided him, made excuses. By this smile she would make up to him for having to slight him.

The smile made really more of an impression than she had bargained for. He dropped his jaw, cleared his throat, blew his nose, pulled at his pipe, frantically summoned his dogs, murmured something incoherent, raised his cap, and went stamping away. After a bit he stopped, flipped up a toadstool with his stick, demolished some withered stalks of cow-parsley. He breathed deeply, saying Hmmmmmm . . . Then he said: 'I'll be damned.' He looked round; but her skirts, her legs were just swinging round the corner.

Olivia went on down the path, feeling cheerful. When she got to the tile she laughed out loud, thinking what a surprise she had given him.

Arthur Koestler   Arthur Koestler was born in Budapest in
1905. He studied psychology at the University of Vienna and became a journalist when
he was 21. As a foreign correspondent he
lived in the Middle East, Paris and Moscow.
He was at this time a member of the Communist Party.

In 1937 whilst working for the *News
Chronicle* with the loyalist forces in Spain he
was captured by General Franco's troops and
held for three months in prison under sentence of death. An account of these experiences is to be found in his book *Spanish
Testament* (1938).

About this time he left the Communist
Party; in 1949 he was to contribute to *The
God that Failed*, a collection of studies by ex-communists. In 1940 came the novel *Darkness at Noon*, written in German. During
the war Koestler served in the British Army
and since the war he has lived in England.

Arthur Koestler is still deeply interested in
psychology and systems of thought. 'I
travelled in India and Japan (in 1958–9) in
the mood of the pilgrim. I wondered whether the East had any answer to offer to
our own perplexities and dead-locked problems.' His conclusions are to be found in *The
Lotus and the Robot* (1960). In 1964 he published *The Act of Creation*, a study of the
intellectual nature of scientific discovery and
artistic creation.

Darkness at Noon   **Rubashov's Arrest**

*'The characters in this book are fictitious. The historical circumstances which determined their actions are real. The life of the man N. S. Rubashov is a synthesis
of the lives of a number of men who were victims of the so-called Moscow Trials.*

Several of them were personally known to the author.' This passage is contained in a foreword to the novel.

Rubashov, 'former member of the Central Committee of the Party, former Commissar of the People, former Commander of the 2nd Division of the Revolutionary Army, bearer of the Revolutionary Order for Fearlessness before the Enemy of the People', was one of the intellectuals who had taken a leading part in the 1917 Revolution and built up the Communist régime. For forty years he had been guided by communist principles and held important posts. But in 1939 he was arrested.

For most of his adult life as a Communist it was an article of faith with him that any action was justified, however ruthless, if it served the interests of Communism. But in the nineteen-twenties and -thirties No. 1 decided what was in the interests of Communism, and anyone who thought differently was denounced as an enemy of the people and in danger of liquidation. Increasingly in recent years Rubashov had become sensitive to the fate of individual people, haunted more often by Richard the nineteen-year-old German, by Loewy the dockworker; and by Arlova, his secretary, whose lover he had been. Arlova had appealed to him for support in facing a false accusation; he had betrayed her 'in the interests of the state'. Rubashov had not committed any act of sabotage, certainly not of treason, when he was arrested; simply, No. 1 had perceived a subtle change in his attitude.

Darkness at Noon casts light upon events and theories of great importance; and also, like all great novels, it helps us towards an understanding of human nature.

At the front door stood the car in which the officials had come, a new American make. It was still dark; the chauffeur had put on the headlights, the street was asleep or pretended to be. They got in, first the lad, then Rubashov, then the elder official. The chauffeur, who was also in uniform, started the car. Beyond the corner, the asphalt surface stopped; they were still in the centre of the town; all round them were big modern buildings of nine and ten stories, but the roads were country cart-tracks of frozen mud, with a thin powdering of snow in the cracks. The chauffeur drove at a walking pace and the superbly sprung motor car creaked and groaned like an ox-wagon.

'Drive faster,' said the lad, who could not bear the silence in the car.

The chauffeur shrugged his shoulders without looking round. He had given Rubashov an indifferent and unfriendly look as he got into the car. Rubashov had once had an accident; the man at the wheel of the ambulance-car had looked at him in the same way. The slow, jolting drive through the dead streets, with the wavering light of the headlamps before them, was difficult to stand. 'How far is it?' asked Rubashov, without looking at his companions. He nearly added: to the hospital. 'A good half-hour,' said the older man in uniform. Rubashov dug cigarettes out of his pocket, put one in his mouth and passed the packet round automatically. The young man refused abruptly, the elder one took two and passed one on to the chauffeur. The chauffeur touched his cap and gave everybody a light, holding the steering-wheel with one hand. Rubashov's heart became lighter; at the same time he was annoyed with himself for it. Just the time to get sentimental, he thought. But he could not resist the temptation to speak and to awaken a little human warmth around him. 'A pity for the car,' he said. 'Foreign cars cost quite a bit of gold, and after half a year on our roads they are finished.'

'There you are quite right. Our roads are very backward,' said the old official. By this time Rubashov realized that he had understood his helplessness. He felt like a dog to whom one had just thrown a bone; he decided not to speak again. But suddenly the boy said aggressively:

'Are they any better in the capitalist states?'

Rubashov had to grin. 'Were you ever outside?' he asked.

'I know all the same what it is like there,' said the boy. 'You need not try to tell me stories about it.'

'Whom do you take me for, exactly?' asked Rubashov very quietly. But he could not prevent himself from adding: 'You really ought to study the Party history a bit.'

The boy was silent and looked fixedly at the driver's back. Nobody spoke. For the third time the driver choked off the panting engine and let it in again, cursing. They jolted through the suburbs; in the appearance of the miserable wooden houses nothing was changed. Above their crooked silhouettes hung the moon, pale and cold.

In every corridor of the new model prison electric light was burning. It lay bleakly on the iron galleries, on the bare whitewashed walls, on the cell doors with the name cards and the black holes of the judas-eyes. This colourless light, and the shrill echoless sound of their steps on the tiled paving were so familiar to Rubashov that for a few seconds he played with the illusion that he was dreaming again. He tried to make himself believe

G

that the whole thing was not real. If I succeed in believing that I am dreaming, then it will really be a dream, he thought.

He tried so intensely that he nearly became dizzy; then immediately a choking shame rose in him. This has to be gone through, he thought. Right through to the end. They reached cell No. 404. Above the spy-hole was a card with his name on it. Nicolas Salmanovich Rubashov. They have prepared everything nicely, he thought; the sight of his name on the card made an uncanny impression on him. He wanted to ask the warder for an extra blanket, but the door had already slammed behind him.

At regular intervals the warder had peeped through the judas into Rubashov's cell. Rubashov had been lying tranquilly on the bunk; only his hand had twitched from time to time in his sleep. Beside the bunk lay his pince-nez and a cigarette stump on the tiles.

At seven o'clock in the morning—two hours after he had been brought to cell 404—Rubashov was woken by a bugle call. He had slept dreamlessly, and his head was clear. The bugle repeated three times the same blaring sequence. The trembling tones re-echoed and died out; a malevolent silence remained.

It was not yet quite day; the contours of the can and of the wash-basin were softened by the dim light. The window grate was a black pattern silhouetted against the dingy glass; top left a broken pane had a piece of newspaper stuck over it. Rubashov sat up, reached for the pince-nez and the cigarette stump at the end of his bed and lay back again. He put on the pince-nez and managed to make the stump glow. The silence lasted. In all the whitewashed cells of this honeycomb in concrete, men were simultaneously arising from their bunks, cursing and groping about on the tiles, yet in the isolation cells one heard nothing—except from time to time retreating footsteps in the corridor. Rubashov knew that he was in an isolation cell and that he was to stay there until he was shot. He drew his fingers through his short, pointed beard, smoked his cigarette-end and lay still.

So I shall be shot, thought Rubashov. Blinking, he watched the movement of his big toe, which stuck up vertically at the end of the bed. He felt warm, secure and very tired; he had no objection to dozing straight off into death, there and then, if only one let him remain lying under the warm blanket. 'So they are going to shoot you', he told himself. He slowly moved his toes in the sock and a verse occurred to him which compared the feet of Christ to a white roebuck in a thornbush. He rubbed his pince-nez on his sleeve with the gesture familiar to all his followers. He felt in the warmth of the blanket almost perfectly happy and feared only one thing, to have to get up and move. 'So you are going to be destroyed,' he said to himself half-aloud and lit another cigarette, although only three were left. The first cigarettes on an empty stomach caused him sometimes a slight feeling of drunkenness; and he was already in that peculiar state of excitement familiar to him from former experiences of the nearness of death. He knew at the same time that this condition was reprehensible and, from a certain point of view, unpermissible, but at the moment he felt no inclination to take that point of view. Instead, he observed the play of his stockinged toes. He smiled. A warm wave of sympathy for his own body, for which usually he had no liking, played over him and its imminent destruction filled him with a self-pitying delight. 'The old guard is dead,' he said to himself. 'We are the last.' 'We are going to be destroyed.' 'For golden lads and girls all must, as chimney-sweepers, come to dust . . .' He tried to recall the tune of 'come to dust. . .' but only the words came to him. 'The old guard is dead,' he repeated and tried to remember their faces. He could only recall a few. Of the first Chairman of the International, who had been executed as a traitor, he could only conjure up a piece of check waistcoat over the slightly round belly. He had never worn braces, only leather belts. The second Prime Minister of the Revolutionary State, also executed, had bitten his nails in moments of danger. . . History will rehabilitate you, thought Rubashov, without particular conviction. What does history know of nail-biting? He smoked and thought of the dead, and of the humiliation which had preceded their death. Nevertheless, he could not bring himself to hate No. 1 as he ought to. He had often looked at the colour-print of No. 1 hanging over his bed and tried to hate it. They had, between themselves, given him many names, but in the end it was No. 1 that stuck. The horror which No. 1 emanated above all consisted in the possibility that he was in the right, and that all those whom he killed had to admit, even with the bullet in the back of their necks, that he conceivably might be in the right. There was no certainty; only the appeal to that mocking oracle they called History, who gave her sentence only when the jaws of the appealer had long since fallen to dust.

Rubashov had the feeling that he was being watched through the spyhole. Without looking, he knew that a pupil pressed to the hole was staring into the cell; a moment later the key did actually grind in the heavy lock. It took some time before the door opened. The warder, a little old man in slippers, remained at the door.

'Why didn't you get up?' he asked.

'I am ill,' said Rubashov.

'What is the matter with you? You cannot be taken to the doctor before to-morrow.'

'Toothache,' said Rubashov.

'Toothache, is it?' said the warder, shuffled out and banged the door.

Now I can at least remain lying here quietly, thought Rubashov, but it gave him no more pleasure. The stale warmth of the blanket became a nuisance to him, and he threw it off. He again tried to watch the movement of his toes, but it bored him. In the heel of each sock there was a hole. He wanted to darn them, but the thought of having to knock on the door and request needle and thread from the warder prevented him; the needle would probably be refused him in any case. He had a sudden wild craving for a newspaper. It was so strong that he could smell the printer's ink and hear the crackling and rustling of the pages. Perhaps a revolution had broken out last night, or the head of a state had been murdered, or an American had discovered the means to counteract the force of gravity. His arrest could not be in it yet; inside the country, it would be kept secret for a while, but abroad the sensation would soon leak through, they would print ten-year-old photographs dug out of the newspaper archives and publish a lot of nonsense about him and No. 1. He now no longer wanted a newspaper, but with the same greed desired to know what was going on in the brain of No. 1. He saw him sitting at his desk, elbows propped, heavy and gloomy, slowly dictating to a stenographer. Other people walked up and down while dictating, blew smoke-rings or played with a ruler. No. 1 did not move, did not play, did not blow rings. . . . Rubashov noticed suddenly that he himself had been walking up and down for the last five minutes; he had risen from the bed without realizing it. He was caught again by his old ritual of never walking on the edges of the paving stones, and already knew the pattern by heart. But his thoughts had not left No. 1 for a second, No. 1, who, sitting at his desk and dictating immovably, had gradually turned into his own portrait, into that well-known colour-print, which hung over every bed or sideboard in the country and stared at people with its frozen eyes.

Rubashov walked up and down in the cell, from the door to the window and back, between bunk, wash-basin and bucket, six and a half steps there, six and a half steps back. At the door he turned to the right, at the window to the left: it was an old prison habit; if one did not change the direction of the turn one rapidly became dizzy. What went on in No. 1's brain? He pictured to himself a cross-section through that brain, painted neatly with grey water-colour on a sheet of paper stretched on a drawing-board with drawing-pins. The whorls of grey matter swelled to entrails, they curled round one another like muscular snakes, became vague and misty like the spiral nebulae on astronomical charts. . . . What went on in the inflated grey whorls? One knew everything about the far-away spiral nebulae, but about them nothing. That was probably the reason that history was more of an oracle than a science. Perhaps later, much later, it would be taught by means of tables of statistics, supplemented by such anatomical sections. The teacher would draw on the blackboard an algebraic formula representing the conditions of life of the masses of a particular nation at a particular period: 'Here, citizens, you see the objective factors which conditioned this historical process.' And, pointing with his ruler to a grey foggy landscape between the second and third lobe of No. 1's brain: 'Now here you see the subjective reflection of these factors. It was this which in the second quarter of the twentieth century led to the triumph of the totalitarian principle in the East of Europe.' Until this stage was reached, politics would remain bloody dilettantism, mere superstition and black magic. . . .

Rubashov heard the sound of several people marching down the corridor in step. His first thought was: now the beating-up will start. He stopped in the middle of the cell, listening, his chin pushed forward. The marching steps came to a halt before one of the neighbouring cells, a low command was heard, the keys jangled. Then there was silence.

Rubashov stood stiffly between the bed and the bucket, held his breath, and waited for the first scream. He remembered that the first scream, in which terror still predominated over physical pain, was usually the worst; what followed was already more bearable, one got used to it and after a time one could even draw conclusions on the method of torture from the tone and rhythm of the screams. Towards the end, most people behaved in the same way, however different they were in temperament and voice: the screams became weaker, changed over into whining and choking. Usually the door would slam soon after. The keys would jangle again; and the first scream of the next victim often came even before they had touched him, at the mere sight of the men in the doorway.

Rubashov stood in the middle of his cell and waited for the first scream. He rubbed his glasses on his sleeve and said to himself that he would not scream this time either, whatever happened to him. He repeated this sentence as if praying with a rosary. He stood and waited; the scream still did not come. Then he heard a faint clanging, a voice murmured something, the cell-door slammed. The footsteps moved to the next cell.

Rubashov went to the spy-hole and looked into the corridor. The men stopped nearly opposite his cell, at No. 407. There was the old warder with two orderlies dragging a tub of tea, a third carrying a basket with slices of black bread, and two uniformed officials with pistols. There was no beating-up; they were bringing breakfast. . . .

No. 407 was just being given bread. Rubashov could not see him. No. 407 was presumably standing in the regulation position, a step behind the door; Rubashov could only see his forearms and hands. The arms were bare and very thin; like two parallel sticks, they stuck out of the doorway into the corridor. The palms of the invisible No. 407 were turned upwards, curved in the shape of a bowl. When he had taken the bread, he clasped his hands and withdrew into the darkness of his cell. The door slammed.

Rubashov abandoned the spy-hole and resumed his marching up and down. He ceased rubbing his spectacles on his sleeve, breathed deeply and with relief. He whistled a tune and waited for his breakfast. He remembered with a slight feeling of uneasiness those thin arms and the curved hands; they reminded him vaguely of something he could not define. The outlines of those stretched-out hands and even the shadows on them were familiar to him—familiar and yet gone from his memory like an old tune or the smell of a narrow street in a harbour.

L P Hartley

L. P. Hartley was born in 1895 and educated at Harrow and Balliol College, Oxford. Before the war he was known as the author of two volumes of short stories and the short novel *Simonetta Perkins* (1925). The trilogy about the brother and sister Eustace and Hilda Cherrington—*The Shrimp and the Anemone* (1944), *The Sixth Heaven* (1946) and *Eustace and Hilda* (1947)—is probably his best-known work. Other novels are *The Boat* (1950), *My Fellow Devils* (1951), *The Go-Between* (1953), *A Perfect Woman* (1955), *The Hireling* (1957).

Mr Hartley, a scholarly writer, is in the main tradition of English novelists, concerned with the behaviour of men and women in society, with moral decisions. His main characters are members of the middle-classes and he seems to be most confident when writing about the first quarter of the century.

The Shrimp and the Anemone   The Geography Lesson

In this book Eustace is a little boy, in The Sixth Heaven *an undergraduate at Oxford and in* Eustace and Hilda *a young man mainly on holiday in Venice. He is a contemporary of his creator; he was a little boy, then, in the first decade of the century. Eustace is a sensitive, intelligent and charming boy and he retains these qualities in manhood. His mind is continually unfolding: discovering, discriminationg, absorbing. The first part of* Eustace and Hilda, *for example, is wonderfully evocative of the effect of Venice on the young man's awakening mind.*

In Eustace's boyhood the Cherringtons live in a small holiday resort on the coast of Lincolnshire. Mr Cherrington, a widower, is an accountant. He has three children: Hilda aged twelve, Eustace aged nine and Barbara the baby. Other members of the household are Mr Cherrington's unmarried sister Sarah, Minney the children's nurse, and Annie the maid. Eustace is dominated by Hilda. All the

*adults in the house are concerned, in a bleak Victorian way, for his spiritual wel-
fare, though Minney, perhaps, shows more warmth of feeling than the others.*

The days passed quickly: August would soon be here. Hilda and Eustace
were sitting one on each side of the dining-room table, their lessons in
front of them. Hilda stared at her sketch map of England, Eustace stared
at her; then they both glanced interrogatively and rather nervously at
Aunt Sarah, enthroned between them at the head of the table.

'Rutland,' said Aunt Sarah impressively.

Eustace liked geography; he knew the answer to Rutland, and he was
also aware that Hilda didn't know. When they played 'Counties of England' Rutland invariably stumped her. Eustace pondered. His map was
already thickly studded with county towns while Hilda's presented a
much barer appearance. She wouldn't mind if he beat her, for she always
liked him to excel, indeed she insisted on it; she minded more if he failed
over his lessons than if she did. Often when she reproved him for poor
work he had protested 'Anyhow I did better than you!' and she, not at
all abashed, would reply, 'That's got nothing to do with it. You know
you can do better than that if you try.' The effort to qualify for his
sister's approval was the ruling force in Eustace's interior life: he had to
live up to her idea of him, to fulfil the ambitions she entertained on his
behalf. And though he chafed against her domination it was necessary for
him; whenever, after one of their quarrels, she temporarily withdrew her
jealous supervision saying she didn't care now, he could get his feet wet
and be as silly and lazy and naughty as he liked, she would never bother
about him again, he felt as though the bottom had dropped out of his
life, as though the magnetic north had suddenly repudiated the needle.
Hilda believed that her dominion was founded upon grace: she shouldered
her moral responsibilities towards Eustace without misgiving: she did not
think it necessary to prove or demonstrate her ascendancy by personal
achievements outside the moral sphere. Nor did Eustace think so; but
all the same his comfortable sense of her superiority was troubled whenever she betrayed, as she was certainly doing now, distinct signs of intellectual fallibility. It was painful to him, in cold blood, to expose her to
humiliation even in his thoughts, so with a sigh he checked his pen in mid-
career and refrained from writing Oakham.

'That's all,' said Aunt Sarah a few minutes later. 'Let's count up. And
then I've got something to tell you.'

'Is it something nice?' asked Eustace.

'You always want to know that, Eustace,' said Aunt Sarah not un-kindly. 'I notice that Hilda never does. It is a great mistake, as you will find in after life, always to be wondering whether things are going to be nice or nasty. Usually, you will find, they are neither.'

'Eustace is better now at doing things he doesn't like,' observed Hilda.

'Yes, I think he is. Now, how many towns have you got, Hilda?'

'Twenty-five.'

'That's not at all bad, especially as I sent you out shopping all yesterday morning. And you, Eustace?'

'Thirty-two—no, thirty-one.'

'That's not very many. I expected you to do better than that.'

'But I helped Hilda shopping,' objected Eustace. 'I carried the bread all the way home.'

'He wouldn't go into Lawsons' because he's afraid of the dog.'

'Isn't that rather silly of you, Eustace? If it doesn't hurt Hilda, why should it hurt you?'

'It doesn't like little boys,' said Eustace. 'It growled at Gerald Steptoe when he went in to buy his other pocket-knife.'

'Who wouldn't?' asked Hilda rudely.

'Hilda, I don't think that's very kind. And talking of the Steptoes—but first, what did you leave out, Eustace?'

With many pauses Eustace noted the names of the missing towns.

'And Oakham, too! But you know Oakham perfectly well: or had you forgotten it?'

'Of course he hadn't,' said Hilda with feeling. 'He always remembers it —just because it's not important.'

'No,' said Eustace slowly. 'I hadn't forgotten it.'

'Then why didn't you put it down?'

Eustace considered. He was painfully, scrupulously truthful.

'I didn't want to.'

'Didn't want to! Why, what a funny boy! Why didn't you want to?'

Again Eustace paused. An agony of deliberation furrowed his forehead.

'I thought it was best to leave it out,' he said.

'But, what nonsense! I don't know what's come over you. Well, you must write out twice over the names of the towns you missed, and Oak-ham five times. Hilda, you have been busy, so it will do if you mark them on your map in red ink. Then you can go and play. But first I want to tell you about Thursday.'

'Oh, is it to be Thursday?' asked Eustace.

'Wait a minute. You must learn not to be impatient, Eustace. Thursday may never come. But I was going to say, your father doesn't go to Ouse-mouth on Thursday afternoon so we're all going for a drive.'

'Hurray!' cried both children at once.

'And Mrs Steptoe has very kindly invited us to join them on the Downs for a picnic.'

Hilda looked utterly dismayed at this.

'Do you think we ought to go?' she asked anxiously. 'Last year when we went Eustace was sick after we got home.'

'I wasn't!' Eustace exclaimed. 'I only felt sick.'

'Eustace must try very hard not to get excited,' Aunt Sarah said in a tone that was at once mild and menacing. 'Otherwise he won't be allowed to go again.'

'But he always gets excited,' Hilda persisted, ignoring the faces that Eustace, who had jumped up at the news, was making at her from behind his aunt's back. 'Nancy excites him; he can't really help it.'

Aunt Sarah smiled, and as her features lost their habitual severity of cast they revealed one of the sources from which Hilda got her beauty.

'It's Eustace's fault if he lets Nancy make him behave foolishly,' she said with rather chilly indulgence. 'He must remember she is only a little girl.'

'But she's older than me,' said Eustace. 'She's quite old; she's older than Hilda.'

'In years, perhaps. But not in other ways. Hilda has an old head on young shoulders, haven't you, Hilda?'

At the compliment Hilda smiled through her portentous frowns.

'I'm sure I know better than she does what's good for Eustace,' she announced decidedly.

'Then you must see that he doesn't run about like a little mad thing and over-eat himself,' said Aunt Sarah. 'If you do that everything will be all right.'

'Oh, yes,' cried Eustace ecstatically, 'I'm sure it will. Hilda always tells me to stop playing when I begin to look tired.'

'Yes, I do,' said Hilda a trifle grimly, 'but you don't always stop.'

Aunt Sarah was moving to the door when Eustace called after her. 'May I do my corrections in the nursery?'

'Do you think Minney will want you when she's busy with Baby?'

'Oh, she won't mind if I keep very still.'

'I think I'd better come too,' said Hilda.

'Yes, do come,' said Eustace. 'But mightn't two be more in the way than one?'

'Very well, I'll stay here since you don't want me.'

'I do want you, I do want you!' cried Eustace. 'Only I didn't think there was any red ink in the nursery.'

'That shows all the more you don't want me!' said Hilda. 'When you come down I shall have gone out.'

'Don't go far!'

'I shall go a long way. You won't be able to find me.'

'Where shall you go?'

'Oh, nowhere in particular.' And then as Eustace was closing the door she called out, 'Perhaps towards the lighthouse.'

Eustace knocked at the nursery door. 'It's me, Minney.'

'Come in, Eustace. . . . Goodness gracious! what have you got there?'

She bustled up, a small, active woman with a kind round face and soft tidy hair. 'Whatever's that?'

'It's what I've done wrong,' said Eustace gloomily.

'Is it? Let me look. I don't call that much. I should be very proud if I made no more mistakes than that.'

'Would you?' asked Eustace almost incredulously.

'Yes, I should. I'll be bound Hilda didn't get as many right as you did.'

Eustace considered. 'Of course she's very good at sums . . . But you mustn't let me interrupt you, Minney.'

'Interrupt! Listen to the boy. I've got nothing to do. Baby's outside in the pram, asleep, I hope.'

'Oughtn't one of us to go and look at her, perhaps?'

'Certainly not. Now, what do you want? A table? Here it is. A chair? I'll put it there, and you on it.' Suiting the action to the word, she lifted Eustace, passive and acquiescent, on to the white chair. 'And now what? Ink? I'll go and fetch it.' Poor lamb, she murmured to herself outside the door, how tired he looks!

Left alone, Eustace fell into a reverie. Though he could not have formulated the reason for it, he felt an exquisite sense of relief; the tongues of criticism, that wagged around him all day, at last were stilled.

'Here's the ink,' said Minney, appearing with a great impression of rapid movement, 'and the blotting-paper and a pen. My word, you want a lot of waiting on, don't you?'

'I'm afraid I do,' said Eustace humbly. 'Hilda says you spoil me.'

'What nonsense! But mind you, don't make a mess, or else you'll hear about it.'

'Do you think I'm messy?' asked Eustace anxiously.

'No, you're always a good boy.' This favourable judgement surprised Eustace into a shocked denial.

'Oh no,' he said, as though the idea were blasphemous.

'Yes, you are. You're just like your mother.'

'I wish I could remember her better.'

'Well, you were very young then.'

'Why did she die, Minney?'

'I've told you ever so many times, she died when your sister Barbara was born.'

'But mothers don't always die then.'

'No . . .' said Minney, turning away, 'but she did . . . Now get on, Eustace, or you'll have the whole morning gone.'

Eustace began to write. Presently his tongue came out and followed his pen with sympathetic movements.

'Good gracious, child, don't do that—if the wind changed——'

'I'm sorry, Minney.'

'And don't for heaven's sake sit all hunched up. You'll grow into a question mark.'

Obediently Eustace straightened himself, but the effort of sitting upright and keeping his tongue in was so great that the work proceeded twice as slowly as before.

'That's better,' said Minney, coming and standing behind him, her sewing in her hand. 'But what do you call that letter, a C? It looks more like an L.'

'It's a capital C,' explained Eustace. Oh dear! Here was the voice of criticism again, and coming, most disappointingly, from Minney's mouth. 'Don't you make them like that?'

'No, I don't, but I dare say I'm old-fashioned.'

'Then I like people to be old-fashioned,' said Eustace placatingly.

'I always tell them you'll get on in the world, Eustace. You say such nice things to people.'

'Dear Minney!'

It was delicious to be praised. A sense of luxury invaded Eustace's heart. Get on in the world . . . say nice things to people . . . he would remember that. He was copying 'Oakham' for the fourth time when he heard a shout at the window, repeated a second later still more imperiously, 'Eustace! EUSTACE!'

'Gracious!' said Minney. 'She'll wake the baby. When she wants a thing she never thinks of anyone else.'

Eustace was already at the window. 'Coming, Hilda!' he cried in a raucous whisper. 'I was afraid you'd gone to the lighthouse.'

Graham Greene

Graham Greene was born in 1904. From Berkhamsted School where his father was headmaster he went on to Balliol College, Oxford. For four years he worked on *The Times*. His first novel, *The Man Within*, appeared in 1929, *England Made Me* in 1935. He was now literary editor of *The Spectator*. In 1926 he had been received into the Roman Catholic Church, but his first explicitly Catholic novel, *Brighton Rock*, did not appear until 1938. That year he visited Mexico to report on the position of the Church there. *The Lawless Roads* followed in 1939 and the novel *The Power and the Glory* in 1940.

During the war Graham Greene worked for the Foreign Office and spent the years 1941–3 in Sierra Leone. He is now a director of a publishing firm. Amongst his post-war novels have been *The Quiet American*, *The Heart of the Matter* (1948), *A Burnt-Out Case* and *The End of the Affair*.

The theme of Graham Greene's novels is the conflict between good and evil in men's minds and the setting is always contemporary. He is obsessed by what seems to him the meaninglessness of the lives of men who have no faith. A critic has said that 'seedy' is Greene's favourite word; it may be, but he uses the word 'pity' more frequently.

Graham Greene divides his fiction into novels and 'entertainments'; amongst the latter are *The Ministry of Fear* (1943) and *Our Man in Havana* (1958).

The Heart of the Matter **Young Pemberton**

Major Scobie, a man of fifty, was Deputy Commissioner of Police in a West African colony. He loved his wife Louise and he came to love Helen Rolt— love to Scobie meaning pity, compassion, responsibility. 'He had no sense of responsibility toward the beautiful and the graceful and the intelligent. They could find their own way. It was the face for which nobody would go out of his way, the face that would never catch the covert look, the face which would soon be used to rebuffs and indifference that demanded his allegiance. The word "pity" is used as loosely as the word "love"; the terrible promiscuous passion which so few experience.' Scobie's love led him to acts which as a Roman Catholic he believed to be evil.

Here Scobie, accompanied by his servant Ali, is visiting the police post at Bamba. The post has been under the command of Pemberton, a twenty-five-year-old officer.

'One hour more,' Ali said, and he noticed that the darkness was thinning. 'Another mug of tea, Ali, and put some whisky in it.' The convoy had separated from them a quarter of an hour ago, when the police van had turned away from the main road and bumped along a by-road farther into the bush. He shut his eyes and tried to draw his mind away from the broken peal of figures to the distasteful job. There was only a native police sergeant at Bamba, and he would like to be clear in his own mind as to what had happened before he received the sergeant's illiterate report. It would be better, he considered reluctantly, to go first to the Mission and see Father Clay.

Father Clay was up and waiting for him in the dismal little mission house which had been built among the mud huts in laterite bricks to look like a Victorian presbytery. A hurricane lamp shone on the priest's short red hair and his young freckled Liverpool face. He couldn't sit still for more than a few minutes at a time, and then he would be up, pacing his tiny room from hideous oleograph to plaster statue and back to oleograph again. 'I saw so little of him', he wailed, motioning with his hands as though he were at the altar. 'He cared for nothing but cards and drinking. I don't drink and I've never played cards—except demon, you know, except demon, and that's a patience. It's terrible, terrible.'

'He hanged himself?'

'Yes. His boy came over to me yesterday. He hadn't seen him since the night before, but that was quite usual after a bout, you know, a bout. I told him to go to the police. That was right, wasn't it? There was nothing I could do. Nothing. He was quite dead.'

'Quite right. Would you mind giving me a glass of water and some aspirin?'

'Let me fix the aspirin for you. You know, Major Scobie, for weeks and months nothing happens here at all. I just walk up and down here, up and down, and then suddenly out of the blue . . . it's terrible.' His eyes were red and sleepless: he seemed to Scobie one of those who are quite unsuited to loneliness. There were no books to be seen except a little shelf with his breviary and a few religious tracts. He was a man without resources. He began to pace up and down again and suddenly, turning on Scobie, he shot out an excited question. 'Mightn't there be a hope that it's murder?'

'Hope?'

'Suicide,' Father Clay said. 'It's too terrible. It puts a man outside mercy. I've been thinking about it all night.'

'He wasn't a Catholic. Perhaps that makes a difference. Invincible ignorance, eh?'

'That's what I try to think.' Half-way between oleograph and statuette he suddenly started and stepped aside as though he had encountered another on his tiny parade. Then he looked quickly and slyly at Scobie to see whether his act had been noticed.

'How often do you get down to the port?' Scobie asked.

'I was there for a night nine months ago. Why?'

'Everybody needs a change. Have you many converts here?'

'Fifteen. I try to persuade myself that young Pemberton had time— time, you know, while he died, to realise . . .'

'Difficult to think clearly when you are strangling, Father.' He took a swig at the aspirin and the sour grains stuck in his throat. 'If it was murder you'd simply change your mortal sinner, Father,' he said with an attempt at humour which wilted between the holy picture and the holy statue.

'A murderer has time . . .' Father Clay said. He added wistfully, with nostalgia, 'I used to do duty sometimes at Liverpool Gaol.'

'Have you any idea why he did it?'

'I didn't know him well enough. We didn't get on together.'

'The only white men here. It seems a pity.'

'He offered to lend me some books, but they weren't at all the kind of books I care to read—love stories, novels . . .'

'What do you read, Father?'

'Anything on the saints, Major Scobie. My great devotion is to the Little Flower.'

'He drank a lot, didn't he? Where did he get it from?'

'Yusef's store, I suppose.'

'Yes. He may have been in debt?'

'I don't know. It's terrible, terrible.'

Scobie finished his aspirin. 'I suppose I'd better go along.' It was day now outside, and there was a peculiar innocence about the light, gentle and clear and fresh before the sun climbed.

'I'll come with you, Major Scobie.'

The police sergeant sat in a deck-chair outside the D.C.'s bungalow. He rose and raggedly saluted, then immediately in his hollow unformed voice began to read his report. 'At 3.30 p.m. yesterday, sah, I was woken by D.C.'s boy, who reported that D.C. Pemberton, sah . . .'

'That's all right, sergeant, I'll just go inside and have a look round.' The chief clerk waited for him just inside the door.

The living-room of the bungalow had obviously once been the D.C.'s pride—that must have been in Butterworth's day. There was an air of elegance and personal pride in the furniture; it hadn't been supplied by the Government. There were eighteenth-century engravings of the old colony on the wall and in one bookcase were the volumes that Butterworth had left behind him—Scobie noted some titles and authors, Maitland's *Constitutional History*, Sir Henry Maine, Bryce's *Holy Roman Empire*, Hardy's poems, and the *Doomsday Records of Little Withington*, privately printed. But imposed on all this were the traces of Pemberton—a gaudy leather pouf of so-called native work, the marks of cigarette-ends on the chairs, a stack of the books Father Clay had disliked—Somerset Maugham, an Edgar Wallace, two Horlers, and spread-eagled on the settee, *Death Laughs at Locksmiths*. The room was not properly dusted and Butterworth's books were stained with damp.

'The body is in the bedroom, sah,' the sergeant said.

Scobie opened the door and went in—Father Clay followed him. The body had been laid on the bed with a sheet over the face. When Scobie turned the sheet down to the shoulder he had the impression that he was looking at a child in a nightshirt quietly asleep: the pimples were the pimples of puberty and the dead face seemed to bear the trace of no experience beyond the class-room or the football field. 'Poor child,' he said aloud. The pious ejaculation of Father Clay irritated him. It seemed

H   113 to him that unquestionably there must be mercy for someone so unformed. He asked abruptly, 'How did he do it?'

The police sergeant pointed to the picture rail that Butterworth had meticulously fitted—no Government contractor would have thought of it. A picture—an early native king receiving missionaries under a State umbrella—leant against the wall and a cord remained twisted over the brass picture hanger. Who could have expected the flimsy contrivance not to collapse? He can weigh very little, he thought, and he remembered a child's bones, light and brittle as a bird's. His feet when he hung must have been only fifteen inches from the ground.

'Did he leave any papers?' Scobie asked the clerk. 'They usually do.' Men who are going to die are apt to become garrulous with self-revelations.

'Yes, sah, in the office.'

It needed only a casual inspection to realize how badly the office had been kept. The filing cabinet was unlocked: the trays on the desk were filled by papers dusty with inattention. The native clerk had obviously followed the same ways as his chief. 'There, sah, on the pad.'

Scobie read, in a hand-writing as unformed as the face, a script-writing which hundreds of his school contemporaries must have been turning out all over the world: *Dear Dad,—Forgive all this trouble. There doesn't seem anything else to do. It's a pity I'm not in the army because then I might be killed. Don't go and pay the money I owe—the fellow doesn't deserve it. They may try and get it out of you. Otherwise I wouldn't mention it. It's a rotten business for you, but it can't be helped. Your loving son.* The signature was 'Dicky'. It was like a letter from school excusing a bad report.

He handed the letter to Father Clay. 'You are not going to tell me there's anything unforgivable there, Father. If you or I did it, it would be despair—I grant you anything with us. We'd be damned all right because we know, but *he* doesn't know a thing.'

'The Church's teaching . . .'

'Even the Church can't teach me that God doesn't pity the young . . .' Scobie broke abruptly off. 'Sergeant, see that a grave's dug quickly before the sun gets too hot. And look out for any bills he owed. I want to have a word with someone about this.' When he turned towards the window the light dazzled him. He put his hand over his eyes and said, 'I wish to God my head . . .' and shivered. 'I'm in for a dose if I can't stop it. If you don't mind Ali putting up my bed at your place, Father, I'll try and sweat it out.'

Kingsley Amis

Kingsley Amis was born in London in 1922 and educated at the City of London School and St John's College, Oxford. His university career was interrupted by war service in the army. He lectured in English Literature at University College, Swansea, from 1949 to 1961, when he was appointed to a Fellowship at Peterhouse, Cambridge. He resigned his Fellowship in 1963 in order to devote more time to writing.

Mr Amis's novels are *Lucky Jim* (1954), *That Uncertain Feeling* (1955), *I Like it Here* (1958), *Take a Girl Like You* (1960) and *One Fat Englishman* (1963). *A Frame of Mind* and *A Case of Samples* are collections of poetry. *New Maps of Hell* (1961) is a survey of science fiction.

In the course of his review of *Lucky Jim* in 1954, Walter Allen wrote, 'A new hero has arisen among us. Is he the intellectual tough or the tough intellectual? He is consciously, even conscientiously, graceless. His face, when not dead-pan, is set in a snarl of exasperation. He has one skin too few, but his is not the sensitiveness of the young man in earlier twentieth-century fiction: it is to the phoney that his nerve-ends are tremblingly exposed, and at the least suspicion of the phoney he goes tough. He is at odds with his conventional university education, though he comes generally from a famous university: he has seen through the academic racket as he sees through all the others. A racket is phoney-ness organized, and in contact with phoney-ness he turns red just as litmus paper does in contact with acid. In life he has been among us for some little time. One may speculate whence he derives. The Services, certainly, helped to make him; but George Orwell, Dr Leavis and the Logical Positivists—or, rather, the attitudes these represent—all contributed to his genesis. In fiction I think he first arrived last year, as the central character of Mr John Wain's novel *Hurry on Down*. He turns up again in Mr Amis's *Lucky Jim*.'

Lucky Jim   A Contribution to Knowledge

James Dixon, B.A., is in his third term as history lecturer at the university.

Where was Welch? The old man was well known for an incurable evader. Dixon flung himself up the staircase, past the memorial plaques, and along the deserted corridors, but the familiar low-ceilinged room was empty. He clattered down the back stairs, an escape-route he often used himself, and into the Staff Cloakroom. Welch was in there, stooped secretively over a wash-basin. 'Ah, just caught you,' Dixon said convivially. 'Thought you'd gone without me. Professor,' he added, nearly too late.

The other raised his narrow face, distorted with wonder. 'Gone?' he asked. 'You're . . .'

'You're taking me home for tea,' Dixon enunciated. 'We arranged it on Monday, at coffee-time, in the Common Room.' He caught sight of his own face in the wall-mirror and was surprised to see that it wore an expression of eager friendliness.

Welch had been flicking water from his hands, a movement he now arrested. He looked like an African savage being shown a simple conjuring trick. He said: 'Coffee-time?'

'Yes, on Monday,' Dixon answered him, putting his hands into his pockets and bunching the fists.

'Oh,' Welch said, and looked at Dixon for the first time. 'Oh. Did we say this afternoon?' He turned aside to a streaked roller-towel and began a slow drying of his hands, watching Dixon alertly.

'That's right, Professor. Hope it's still convenient.'

'Oh, it's convenient enough,' Welch said in an unnaturally quiet voice.

'Good,' Dixon said, 'I'm looking forward to it,' and took his dirty old raincoat from a hook in the wall.

Welch's manner was still a little veiled, but he was obviously recovering quickly, and managed quite soon to pick up his 'bag' and put his fawn fishing-hat on his head. 'We'll go down in my car,' he offered.

'That'll be nice.'

Outside the building they turned along a gravel drive and went up to the car where it was parked with a few others. Dixon stared about him while Welch looked thoroughly for his keys. An ill-kept lawn ran down in front of them to a row of amputated railings, beyond which was College Road and the town cemetery, a conjunction responsible for some popular local jokes. Lecturers were fond of lauding to their students the comparative receptivity to facts of 'the Honours class over the road', while the parallel between the occupations of graveyard attendant and custodian of learning was one which often suggested itself to others besides the students.

As Dixon watched, a bus passed slowly up the hill in the mild May sunshine, bound for the small town where the Welches lived. Dixon betted himself it would be there before them. A roaring voice began to sing behind one of the windows above his head; it sounded like, and presumably might even be, Barclay, the Professor of Music.

A minute later Dixon was sitting listening to a sound like the ringing of a cracked door-bell as Welch pulled at the starter. This died away into a treble humming that seemed to involve every component of the car. Welch tried again; this time the effect was of beer-bottles jerkily belaboured. Before Dixon could do more than close his eyes he was pressed firmly back against the seat, and his cigarette, still burning, was cuffed out of his hand into some interstice of the floor. With a tearing of gravel under the wheels the car burst from a standstill towards the grass verge, which Welch ran over briefly before turning down the drive. They moved towards the road at walking pace, the engine maintaining a loud lowing sound which caused a late group of students, most of them wearing the yellow and green College scarf, to stare after them from the small covered-in space beside the lodge where sports notices were posted.

They climbed College Road, holding to the middle of the highway. The unavailing hoots of a lorry behind them made Dixon look furtively at Welch, whose face, he saw with passion, held an expression of calm assurance, like an old quartermaster's in rough weather. Dixon shut his eyes again. He was hoping that when Welch had made the second of the two maladroit gear-changes which lay ahead of him, the conversation would turn in some other direction than the academic. He even thought he'd rather hear some more about music or the doings of Welch's sons, the effeminate writing Michel and the bearded pacifist painting Bertrand whom Margaret had described to him. But whatever the subject for discussion might be, Dixon knew that before the journey ended he'd find his face becoming creased and flabby, like an old bag, with the strain of making it smile and show interest and speak its few permitted words, of steering it between a collapse into helpless fatigue and a tautening with anarchic fury.

'Oh . . . uh . . . Dixon.'

Dixon opened his eyes, doing everything possible with the side of his face away from Welch, everything which might help to relieve his feelings in advance. 'Yes, Professor?'

'I was wondering about that article of yours.'

'Oh yes. I don't . . .'

'Have you heard from Partington yet?'

'Well yes, actually I sent it to him first of all, if you remember, and he said the pressure of other stuff was . . .'

'What?'

Dixon had lowered his voice below the medium shout required by the noise of the car, in an attempt to half-conceal from Welch Welch's own lapse of memory, and so protect himself. Now he had to bawl out: 'I told you he said he couldn't find room for its . . .'

'Oh, couldn't he? Couldn't he? Well, of course they do get a lot of the most . . . a most terrific volume of stuff sent to them, you know. Still, I suppose if anything really took their eye, then they . . . they . . . Have you sent it off to anyone ele?'

'Yes, that Caton chap who advertised in the *T.L.S.* a couple of months ago. Starting up a new historical review with an international bias, or something. I thought I'd get in straight away. After all, a new journal can't very well be bunged up as far ahead as all the ones I've . . .'

'Ah yes, a new journal might be worth trying. There was one advertised in the *Times Literary Supplement* a little while ago. Paton or some such name the editor fellow was called. You might have a go at him, now that it doesn't seem as if any of the more established reviews have got room for your . . . effort. Let's see now; what's the exact title you've given it?'

Dixon looked out of the window at the fields wheeling past, bright green after a wet April. It wasn't the double-exposure effect of the last half-minute's talk that had dumbfounded him, for such incidents formed the staple material of Welch colloquies; it was the prospect of reciting the title of the article he'd written. It was a perfect title, in that it crystallized the article's niggling mindlessness, its funereal parade of yawn-enforcing facts, the pseudo-light it threw upon non-problems. Dixon had read, or begun to read, dozens like it, but his own seemed worse than most in its air of being convinced of its own usefulness and significance. 'In considering this strangely neglected topic,' it began. This what neglected topic? This strangely what topic? This strangely neglected what? His thinking all this without having defiled and set fire to the typescript only made him appear to himself as more of a hypocrite and fool. 'Let's see,' he echoed Welch in a pretended effort of memory: 'oh yes; *The Economic Influence of the Developments in Shipbuilding Techniques, 1450 to 1485.* After all, that's what it's . . .'

Unable to finish his sentence, he looked to his left again to find a man's face staring into his own from about nine inches away. The face, which filled with alarm as he gazed, belonged to the driver of a van which Welch had elected to pass on a sharp bend between two stone walls. A huge bus now swung into view from further round the bend. Welch slowed slightly, thus ensuring that they would still be next to the van when the bus reached them, and said with decision: 'Well, that ought to do it nicely, I should say.'

Before Dixon could roll himself into a ball or even take off his glasses, the van had braked and disappeared, the bus-driver, his mouth opening and shutting vigorously, had somehow squirmed his vehicle against the far wall, and, with an echoing rattle, the car darted forward on to the straight. Dixon, though on the whole glad at this escape, felt at the same time that the conversation would have been appropriately rounded off by Welch's death. He felt this more keenly when Welch went on:' If I were you, Dixon, I should take all the steps I possibly could to get this article accepted in the next month or so. I mean, I haven't the specialized knowledge to judge . . .' His voice quickened: 'I can't tell, can I? what it's worth. It's no use anybody coming to me and asking "What's young Dixon's stuff like?" unless I can give them an expert opinion of what it's worth, is it now? But an acceptance by a learned journal would . . . would . . . You, well you don't know what it's worth yourself, how can you?'

Dixon felt that, on the contrary, he had a good idea of what his article was worth from several points of view. From one of these, the thing's worth could be expressed in one short hyphenated indecency; from another, it was worth the amount of frenzied fact-grubbing and fana-

tical boredom that had gone into it. From yet another, it was worthy
of its aim, the removal of the 'bad impression' he'd so far made in the
College and in his Department. But he said: 'No, of course not, Professor.'

'And you see, Faulkner, it's rather important to you that it should turn
out to be worth something, if you see what I mean.'

Despite being wrongfully addressed (Faulkner had preceded him in his
post), Dixon knew what Welch meant, and said so. How had he made his
bad impression? The most likely thing, he'd always thought, was his having inflicted a superficial wound on the Professor of English in his first
week. This man, a youngish ex-Fellow of a Cambridge college, had been
standing on the front steps when Dixon, coming round the corner from
the library, had kicked violently at a small round stone lying on the
macadam. Before reaching the top of its trajectory it had struck the other
just below the left kneecap at a distance of fifteen yards or more. Averting
his head, Dixon had watched in terrified amzement; it had been useless to
run, as the nearest cover was far beyond reach. At the moment of impact
he'd turned and begun to walk down the drive, but knew well enough
that he was the only visible entity capable of stone-propulsion. He looked
once and saw the Professor of English huddled up on one leg and looking
at him. As always on such occasions, he'd wanted to apologize but had
found, when it came to it, that he was too frightened to. He'd found the
same when, two days later, he'd been passing behind the Registrar's
chair at the first Faculty meeting, had stumbled and knocked the chair
aside just as the other man was sitting down. A warning shout from the
Registrar's Clerk had averted complete disaster, but he could still remember the look on the face of that figure, stiffened in the shape of a letter S.
Then there'd been that essay written for Welch by one of the Honours
people, containing, in fact consisting of, abuse of a book on enclosures by,
it transpired, one of Welch's own ex-pupils. 'I asked him who could
possibly have filled his head with stuff like that, you see, and he said it was
all out of one of your lectures, Dixon. Well, I told him as tactfully as I
could . . .' Much later Dixon had found out that the book in question had
been written at Welch's suggestion and, in part, under his advice. These
facts had been there for all to read in the Acknowledgements, but Dixon,
whose policy it was to read as little as possible of any given book, never
bothered with these, and it had been Margaret who'd told him. That had
been, as near as he could remember, on the morning before the evening
when Margaret had tried to kill herself with sleeping-pills.

When Welch said in a far-away half-shout 'Oh, by the way, Dixon,' Dixon turned to him with real avidity. 'Yes, Professor?' How much better to have more of what Welch could provide than thoughts of what Margaret would provide—commodities which he would in any case soon be sampling in their real form.

'I've been wondering if you'd care to come over next week-end for the . . . week-end. I think it should be quite good fun. We've having a few people from London, you know, friends of ours and of my son Bertrand's. Bertrand's going to try and come himself, of course, but he doesn't know yet if he can get away. I expect we shall put on one or two little shows, little bits of music and that. We'll probably call on you to lend a hand with something.'

The car buzzed on along a clear road. 'Thank you very much, I should love to come,' Dixon said, thinking he must get Margaret to do some intelligence work on the something he'd probably be called upon to lend a hand with.

Welch seemed quite cheered by this ready acceptance. 'That's fine,' he said with apparent feeling. 'Now there's something on the academic side I'd like to discuss with you. I've been talking to the Principal about the College Open Week at the end of term. He wants the History Department to throw something into the pool, you see, and I've been wondering about you.'

'Oh, really?' Surely there were others better qualified to be thrown into the pool?

'Yes, I thought you might care to tackle the evening lecture the Department's going to provide, if you could.'

'Well, I would rather like to have a crack at a public lecture, if you think I'm capable of it,' Dixon managed to say.

'I thought something like "Merrie England" might do as a subject. Not too academic, and not too . . . not too . . . Do you think you could get something together along those sort of lines?'

William Golding

William Golding was born at St Columb Minor, Cornwall, in 1911, and educated at Marlborough Grammar School and Brasenose College, Oxford. During the war he served in the Royal Navy and in 1945 joined the staff of Bishop Wordsworth's School, Salisbury.

Mr Golding had written a good deal of poetry before his first novel, *Lord of the Flies*, was published in 1954. His other novels are *The Inheritors* (1955), *Pincher Martin* (1956), *The Fall* (1959) and *The Spire* (1964). The novels are allegories, the reality symbolic; beneath the surface action are statements about the nature of man. Mr Golding believes that our hold on civilization is tenuous.

Lord of the Flies   Hunting the Beast

An aeroplane has crash-landed and a party of schoolboys find themselves cast away on a tropical island in the Pacific. No adult has survived with them. At first all goes well: a leader is chosen and rules are accepted. Quite soon though, this heritage of civilization which they have brought with them is destroyed, not by an external enemy, but by their own natures.

In 1858 The Coral Island by R. M. Ballantyne was published. Its heroes Ralph, Jack and Peterkin were cast away on a remote island. They lived busy civilized and civilizing lives, even curing the natives of cannibalism. The Victorian optimism which informed The Coral Island has gone; the mid-twentieth century writer has a different view of man, if only because he has lived through the Nazi period. The twins Sam and Eric rushed in terror down the mountainside believing that they had been pursued by a beast. Ralph and Jack are leading a party of boys in search of it. 'Littluns' is the term used by the older boys for the little boys on the island.

The pig-run kept close to the jumble of rocks that lay down by the water on the other side and Ralph was content to follow Jack along it. If you could shut your ears to the slow suck down of the sea and boil of the return, if you could forget how dun and unvisited were the ferny coverts on either side, then there was a chance that you might put the beast out of mind and dream for a while. The sun had swung over the vertical and the afternoon heat was closing in on the island. Ralph passed a message forward to Jack and when they next came to fruit the whole party stopped and ate.

Sitting, Ralph was aware of the heat for the first time that day. He pulled distastefully at his grey shirt and wondered whether he might undertake the adventure of washing it. Sitting under what seemed an unusual heat, even for this island, Ralph planned his toilet. He would like to have a pair of scissors and cut this hair—he flung the mass back— cut this filthy hair right back to half an inch. He would like to have a bath, a proper wallow with soap. He passed his tongue experimentally over his teeth and decided that a toothbrush would come in handy too. Then there were his nails——

Ralph turned his hand over and examined them. They were bitten down to the quick though he could not remember when he had restarted this habit nor any time when he indulged it.

'Be sucking my thumb next——'

He looked round, furtively. Apparently no one had heard. The hunters sat, stuffing themselves with this easy meal, trying to convince themselves that they got sufficient kick out of bananas and that other olive-grey, jelly-like fruit. With the memory of his sometime clean self as a standard, Ralph looked them over. They were dirty, not with the spectacular dirt of boys who have fallen into mud or been brought down hard on a rainy day. Not one of them was an obvious subject for a shower, and yet—hair, much too long, tangled here and there, knotted round a dead leaf or a twig; faces cleaned fairly well by the process of eating and sweating but marked in the less accessible angles with a kind of shadow; clothes, worn away, stiff like his own with sweat, put on, not for decorum or comfort but out of custom; the skin of the body, scurfy with brine——

He discovered with a little fall of the heart that these were the conditions he took as normal now and that he did not mind. He sighed and pushed away the stalk from which he had stripped the fruit. Already the hunters were stealing away to do their business in the woods or down by the rocks. He turned and looked out to sea.

Here, on the other side of the island, the view was utterly different. The filmy enchantments of mirage could not endure the cold ocean water and the horizon was hard, clipped blue. Ralph wandered down to the rocks. Down here, almost on a level with the sea, you could follow with your eye the ceaseless, bulging passage of the deep sea waves. They were miles wide, apparently not breakers or the banked ridges of shallow water. They travelled the length of the island with an air of disregarding it and being set on other business; they were less a progress than a monstrous rise and fall of the whole ocean. Now the sea would suck down, making cascades and waterfalls of retreating water, would sink past the rocks and plaster down the seaweed like shining hair: then, pausing, gather and rise with a roar, irresistibly swelling over point and outcrop, climbing the little cliff, sending at last an arm of surf up a gully to end a yard or so from him in fingers of spray.

Wave after wave, Ralph followed the rise and fall until something of the remoteness of the sea numbed his brain. Then gradually the almost infinite size of this water forced itself on his attention. This was the divider, the barrier. On the other side of the island, swathed at midday with mirage, defended by the shield of quiet lagoon, one might dream of rescue; but here, faced by the brute obtuseness of the ocean, the miles of division, one was clamped down, one was helpless, one was condemned, one was——

Simon was speaking almost in his ear. Ralph found that he had rock painfully gripped in both hands, found his body arched, the muscles of his neck stiff, his mouth strained open.

'You'll get back to where you came from.'

Simon nodded as he spoke. He was kneeling on one knee, looking down from a higher rock which he held with both hands; his other leg stretched down to Ralph's level.

Ralph was puzzled and searched Simon's face for a clue.

'It's so big, I mean——'

Simon nodded.

'All the same. You'll get back all right. I think so, anyway.'

Some of the strain had gone from Ralph's body. He glanced at the sea and then smiled bitterly at Simon.

'Got a ship in your pocket?'

Simon grinned and shook his head.

'How do you know, then?'

When Simon was still silent Ralph said curtly, 'You're batty.'

Simon shook his head violently till the coarse black hair flew backwards and forwards across his face.

'No, I'm not. I just *think you'll get back all right.*'

For a moment nothing more was said. And then they suddenly smiled at each other.

Roger called from the coverts.

'Come and see!'

The ground was turned over near the pig-run and there were drop-pings that steamed. Jack bent down to them as though he loved them.

'Ralph—we need meat even if we are hunting the other thing.'

'If you mean going the right way, we'll hunt.'

They set off again, the hunters bunched a little by fear of the mentioned beast, while Jack quested ahead. They went more slowly than Ralph had bargained for; yet in a way he was glad to loiter, cradling his spear. Jack came up against some emergency of his craft and soon the procession stopped. Ralph leaned against a tree and at once the day-dreams came swarming up. Jack was in charge of the hunt and there would be time to get to the mountain——

Once, following his father from Chatham to Devonport, they had lived in a cottage on the edge of the moors. In the succession of houses that Ralph had known, this one stood out with particular clarity because after that house he had been sent away to school. Mummy had still been with them and Daddy had come home every day. Wild ponies came to the stone wall at the bottom of the garden, and it had snowed. Just behind the cottage there was a sort of shed and you could lie up there, watching the flakes swirl past. You could see the damp spot where each flake died; then you could mark the first flake that lay down without melting and watch the whole ground turn white. You could go indoors when you were cold and look out of the window, past that bright copper kettle and the plate with the little blue men——

When you went to bed there was a bowl of cornflakes with sugar and cream. And the books—they stood on the shelf by the bed, leaning to-gether with always two or three laid flat on top because he had not bothered to put them back properly. They were dog-eared and scratched. There was the bright, shining one about Topsy and Mopsy that he never read because it was about two girls: there was the one about the Magi-cian which you read with a kind of tied-down terror, skipping page twenty-seven with the awful picture of the spider; there was a book about people who had dug things up, Egyptian things; there was the *Boy's Book of Trains, The Boy's Book of Ships.* Vividly they came before him; he could have reached up and touched them, could feel the weight and slow slide with which the *Mammoth Book for Boys* would come out and slither down. . . . Everything was all right; everything was good-humoured and friendly.

The bushes crashed ahead of them. Boys flung themselves wildly from the pig track and scrabbled in the creepers, screaming. Ralph saw Jack nudged aside and fall. Then there was a creature bounding along the pig track towards him, with tusks gleaming and an intimidating grunt. Ralph found he was able to measure the distance coldly and take aim. With the boar only five yards away, he flung the foolish wooden stick that he carried, saw it hit the great snout and hang there for a moment. The boar's note changed to a squeal and it swerved aside into the covert. The pig-run filled with shouting boys again, Jack came running back, and poked about in the undergrowth.

'Through here——'

'But he'd do us!'

'Through here, I said——'

The boar was floundering away from them. They found another pig-run parallel to the first and Jack raced away. Ralph was full of fright and apprehension and pride.

'I hit him! The spear stuck in——'

Now they came, unexpectedly, to an open space by the sea. Jack cast about on the bare rock and looked anxious.

'He's gone.'

'I hit him,' said Ralph again, 'and the spear stuck in a bit.'

He felt the need of witnesses.

'Didn't you see me?'

Maurice nodded.

'I saw you. Right bang on his snout—Wheee!'

Ralph talked on, excitedly.

'I hit him all right. The spear stuck in. I wounded him!'

He sunned himself in their new respect and felt that hunting was good after all.

'I walloped him properly. That was the beast, I think!' Jack came back.

'That wasn't the beast. That was a boar.'

'I hit him.'

'Why didn't you grab him? I tried——'

Ralph's voice ran up.

'But a boar!'

Jack flushed suddenly.

'You said he'd do us. What did you want to throw for? Why didn't you wait?'

He held out his arm.

'Look.'

He turned his left forearm for them all to see. On the outside was a rip; not much, but bloody.

'He did that with his tusks. I couldn't get my spear down in time.'

Attention focused on Jack.

'That's a wound,' said Simon, 'and you ought to suck it. Like Berengaria.'

Jack sucked.

'I hit him,' said Ralph indignantly. 'I hit him with my spear, I wounded him.'

He tried for their attention.

'He was coming along the path. I threw, like this——'

Robert snarled at him. Ralph entered into the play and everybody laughed. Presently they were all jabbing at Robert who made mock rushes.

Jack shouted.

'Make a ring!'

The circle moved in and round. Robert squealed in mock terror, then in real pain.

'Ow! Stop it! You're hurting!'

The butt end of a spear fell on his back as he blundered among them.

'Hold him!'

They got his arms and legs. Ralph, carried away by a sudden thick excitement, grabbed Eric's spear and jabbed at Robert with it.

'Kill him! Kill him!'

All at once, Robert was screaming and struggling with the strength of frenzy. Jack had him by the hair and was brandishing his knife. Behind him was Roger, fighting to get close. The chant rose ritually, as at the last moment of a dance or a hunt.

'*Kill the pig! Cut his throat! Kill the pig! Bash him in!*'

Ralph too was fighting to get near, to get a handful of that brown, vulnerable flesh. The desire to squeeze and hurt was overmastering.

Jack's arm came down; the heaving circle cheered and made pig-dying noises. Then they lay quiet, panting, listening to Robert's frightened snivels. He wiped his face with a dirty arm, and made an effort to retrieve his status.

'Oh, my bum!'

He rubbed his rump ruefully. Jack rolled over.

'That was a good game.'

'Just a game,' said Ralph uneasily. 'I got jolly badly hurt at rugger once.'

'We ought to have a drum,' said Maurice, 'then we could do it properly.'

Ralph looked at him.

'How properly?'

'I dunno. You want a fire, I think, and a drum, and you keep time to the drum.'

'You want a pig,' said Roger, 'like in a real hunt.'

'Or someone to pretend,' said Jack. 'You could get someone to dress up as a pig and then he could act—you know, pretend to knock me over and all that——'

'You want a real pig,' said Robert, still caressing his rump, 'because you've got to kill him.'

'Use a littlun,' said Jack, and everybody laughed.

Alan Sillitoe

Alan Sillitoe was born in Nottingham in 1928. He left his elementary school when he was fourteen and started work in the Raleigh Bicycle Factory. In 1946 he was called up for the R.A.F. and served in Malaya. In 1948, with a small disability pension on which he could just live in Majorca, he began to write. He had little success until he began to write about the working-class life he knew personally. *Saturday Night and Sunday Morning*, published in 1958, was his first novel. Subsequent novels have been *The General* (1960), *Key to the Door* (1961) and *The Death of William Posters* (1965). *The Rats and other Poems* appeared in 1960. *The Loneliness of the Long Distance Runner* (1959) and *The Ragman's Daughter* (1963) are collections of short stories. *Road to Volgograd* (1964) is an account of a month in Russia in 1963 as a guest of the Writers' Union.

Readers particularly interested in the sociological aspect of literature were excited when Sillitoe's work began to appear, for here was a working-class writer writing about working-class life. This is comparatively rare; perhaps articulateness of the kind needed for writing novels is not a working-class attribute; or perhaps it takes a man out of the working class.

Alan Sillitoe's heroes reject most of the beliefs and institutions of organized society, seeing them apparently as stratagems and devices of the enemy. The Long Distance Runner rejects not only the Borstal governor's philosophy but the institution of private property. Even a shopkeeper with a few pounds in the till is an In-law and therefore an enemy and fair game.

I

Saturday Night and Sunday Morning **Monday Morning**

He lifted a pair of clean overalls from the bedrail and pulled them over his big white feet, taking care not to disturb his brother Sam who, while still in the depths of sleep, rolled himself more advantageously into the large mound of blankets now that Arthur had left the bed. He had often heard Friday described as Black Friday—remembering a Boris Karloff film of years ago—and wondered why this should be. For Friday, being payday, was a good day, and 'black' would be more fitting if applied to Monday. Black Monday. Then there would be some sense in it, when you felt your head big from boozing, throat sore from singing, eyes fogged-up from seeing too many films or sitting in front of the television, and feeling black and wicked because the big grind was starting all over again.

The stairfoot door clicked open.

'Arthur,' his father called, in a deadly menacing Monday-morning voice that made your guts rattle, sounding as if it came from the grave, 'when are yer goin' ter get up? Yer'll be late fer wok.' He closed the stairfoot door quietly so as not to waken the mother and two other sons still at home.

Arthur took a half empty fag packet from the mantelpiece, his comb, a ten-shilling note and a heap of coins that had survived the pubs, bookies' counters, and cadgers, and stuffed them into his pockets.

The bottom door opened again.

'Eh?'

'I 'eard yer the first time,' Arthur said in a whisper.

The door slammed, by way of reply.

A mug of tea was needed, then back to the treadmill. Monday was always the worst; by Wednesday he was broken-in, like a greyhound. Well, anyroad, he thought, there was always Brenda, lovely Brenda who was all right and looked after you well once she's made up her mind to it. As long as Jack didn't find out and try to get his hands around my throat. That'd be the day. By Christ it would. Though my hands would be round his throat first, the nit-witted, unlucky bastard.

He glanced once more around the small bedroom, seeing the wooden double-bed pushed under the window, the glint of a white pot, dilapidated shelves holding Sam's books—rulers, pencils, and rubbers—and a home-made table on which stood his portable wireless set. He lifted the latch as the stairfoot door opened again, and his father poked his head up, ready to tell him in his whispering, menacing, Monday-morning gut-rattle that it was time to come down.

Despite the previous tone of his father's voice Arthur found him sitting at the table happily supping tea. A bright fire burned in the modernised grate—the family had clubbed-up thirty quid to have it done—and the room was warm and cheerful, the table set and tea mashed.

Seaton looked up from his cup. 'Come on, Arthur. You ain't got much time. It's ten past seven, and we've both got to be on by half past. Sup a cup o' tea an' get crackin'.'

Arthur sat down and stretched his legs towards the fire. After a cup and a Woodbine his head was clearer. He didn't feel so bad. 'You'll go blind one day, dad,' he said, for nothing, taking words out of the air for sport, ready to play with the consequences of whatever he might cause.

Seaton turned to him uncomprehendingly, his older head still fuddled. It took ten cups of tea and as many Woodbines to set his temper right after the weekend. 'What do you mean?' he demanded, intractable at any time before ten in the morning.

'Sitting' in front of the TV. You stick to it like glue from six to eleven every night. It can't be good for yer. You'll go blind one day. You're bound to. I read it in the *Post* last week that a lad from the Medders went blind. They might be able to save 'im though, because 'e goes to the Eye Infirmary every Monday, Wensday, an' Friday. But it's a risk.'

His father poured another cup of tea, his black brows taut with anger. Short, stocky Seaton was incapable of irritation or mild annoyance. He was either happy and fussy with everybody, or black-browed with a deep melancholy rage that chose its victims at random. In the last few years his choice of victims had grown less, for Arthur, with his brother Fred, had been through the mill of factory and army and now stood up to him, creating a balance of power that kept the house more or less peaceful.

'I'm sure it never did anybody any harm,' Seaton said. 'Anyway, yer never believe what the papers tell yer, do yer? If yer do then yer want yer brains testin'. They never tell owt but lies. That's one thing I do know.'

'I wouldn't be so sure of that,' Arthur said, flipping a dead Woodbine into the fire. 'Anyway, I know somebody who knows this kid as went blind, so the papers was right for a change. They said they saw this kid bein' led to the Eye Infirmary by 'is mam. It was a rotten shame, they said. A kid of seven. She led 'im along wi' a lead, and the kid had a stick specially made for him, painted white. I heard they was getting him a dog as well to help him along, a wire-haired terrier. There was talk o' standin' him outside the Council House for the rest of his life wi' a tin mug if he don't get any better. His dad's got cancer, an' 'is mam can't afford ter keep him in white sticks an' dogs.'

'Ye're balmy,' Seaton said. 'Go an tell yer stories somewhere else. Not that I'm bothered wi' my eyes anyway. My eyes 'ave allus been good, and allus will be. When I went for my medical in the war they were A1, but I swung the lead and got off 3C,' he added proudly.

The subject was dropped. His father cut several slices of bread and made sandwiches with cold meat left from Sunday dinner. Arthur teased him a lot, but in a way he was glad to see the TV standing in a corner of the living-room, a glossy panelled box looking, he thought, like something plundered from a space-ship. The old man was happy at last, anyway, and he deserved to be happy, after all the years before the war on the dole, five kids and the big miserying that went with no money and no way of getting any. And now he had a sit-down job at the factory, all the Woodbines he could smoke, money for a pint if he wanted one, though he didn't as a rule drink, a holiday somewhere, a jaunt on the firm's trip to Blackpool, and a television set to look into at home. The difference between before the war and after the war didn't bear thinking about. War was a marvellous thing in some ways, when you thought about how happy it had made some people in England. There are no flies on me, Arthur thought.

He stuffed a packet of sandwiches and a flask of tea into his pocket, and waited while his father struggled into a jacket. Once out of doors they were more aware of the factory rumbling a hundred yards away over the high wall. Generators whined all night, and during the day giant milling-machines working away on cranks and pedals in the turnery gave to the terrace a sensation of living within breathing distance of some monstrous being that suffered from a disease of the stomach. Disinfectant-suds, grease and newly-cut steel permeated the air over the suburb of four-roomed houses built around the factory, streets and terraces hanging on to its belly and flanks like calves sucking the udders of some great mother. The factory sent crated bicycles each year from the Despatch Department to waiting railway trucks over Eddison Road, boosting post-war (or perhaps pre-war, Arthur thought, because these days a war could start tomorrow) export trade and trying to sling pontoons over a turbulent unbridgeable river called the Sterling Balance. The thousands that worked there took home good wages. No more short-time like before the war, or getting the sack if you stood ten minutes in the lavatory reading your *Football Post*—if the gaffer got on to you now you could always tell him where to put the job and go somewhere else. And no more running out at dinnertime for a penny bag öf chips to eat with your bread. Now, and about time too, you got fair wages if you worked your backbone to a string of conkers on piecework, and there was a big canteen where you could get a hot dinner for two-bob. With the wages you got you could save up for a motorbike or even an old car, or you could go on a ten-day binge and get rid of all you'd saved. Because it was no use saving your money year after year. A mug's game, since the value of it got less and less and in any case you never knew when the Yanks were going to do something daft like dropping the H-bomb on Moscow. And if they did then you could say ta-ta to everybody, burn your football coupons and betting-slips, and ring up Billy Graham. If you believe in God, which I don't, he said to himself.

'It's a bit nippy,' his father remarked, buttoning his coat as they turned into the street.

'What do you expect for November?' Arthur said. Not that he didn't have an overcoat, but you never went to work in one, not even when snow was on the ground and it was freezing. An overcoat was for going out in at night when you had your Teddy suit on. Living only five minutes from the factory, walking kept you warm on your way there, and once inside at your machine the working of it kept your blood running. Only those that came from Mansfield and Kirkby wore over-coats, because it was cold in the buses.

Fat Mrs Bull the gossiper stood with her fat arms folded over her apron at the yard-end, watching people pass by on their way to work. With pink face and beady eyes, she was a tight-fisted defender of her tribe, queen of the yard because she had lived there for twenty-two years, earning names like 'The News of the World' and the 'Loudspeaker' because she watched the factory go in every morning and afternoon to glean choice gossip for retail later on. Neither Arthur nor his father greeted her as they passed, and neither did they speak to each other until they were half way down the street.

It was long, straight, and cobblestoned, with lamp posts and intersections at regular intervals, terraces branching off here and there. You stepped out of the front door and found yourself on the pavement. Red-ochre had been blackened by soot, paint was faded and cracked, everything was a hundred years old except the furniture inside.

'What will they think on next?' Seaton said, after glancing upwards and seeing a television aerial hooked on to almost every chimney, like a string of radar stations, each installed on the never-never.

They turned on to Eddison Road by the big red-bricked canteen. The November sky was clear and dark-blue, with some stars still showing whitely. 'Everybody'll 'ave little baby 'elicopters,' Arthur answered readily. 'You'll see. Five-bob-a-week-and-misses for ten years and you can go and see your mate at Derby in the lunch-hour.'

'Some 'opes,' the old man scoffed.

'I read it in the paper,' Arthur said. 'It was the one last Thursday, I think, because my snap was wrapped-up in it, that they'll get to the moon in five years. In ten they'll be having cheap-day returns. It's true right enough.'

Seaton laughed. 'You're crackers, Arthur. You'll grow up one day and stop telling these tales. You're nearly twenty-two. You should know better. I thought they'd a cured you on it in the Army, but I can see they didn't.'

'The on'y thing the Army cures you on,' Arthur retorted, 'is never to join the Army again. They're dead good at that.'

'When I was a lad they din't even have wireless sets,' Seaton ruminated. 'And now look at what they've got: television. Pictures in your own 'ouse.'

They were caught by the main ingoing stream: bicycles, buses, motor bikes and pedestrians on a last-minute rush to breach one of the seven gates before half past. Arthur and his father walked in by the hexagonal commissionaires' office, a building in the centre of a wide roadway dividing the factory into two unequal parts. Seaton was on viewing in the three-speed shop, so turned off after a hundred yards.

'See yer't dinnertime, Arthur.'

'Tarr-ar, Dad.'

Arthur walked into a huge corridor, searching an inside pocket for his clocking-in card and noticing, as on every morning since he was fifteen—except for a two-year break in the Army—the factory smell of oil-suds, machinery, and shaved steel that surrounded you with an air in which pimples grew and prospered on your face and shoulders, that would have turned you into one big pimple if you did not spend half an hour over the scullery sink every night getting rid of the biggest bastards. What a life, he thought. Hard work and good wages, and a smell all day that turns your guts.

The bright Monday morning ring of the clocking-in machine made a jarring note, different from the tune that played inside Arthur. It was dead on half past seven. Once in the shop he allowed himself to be swallowed by its diverse noises, walked along lanes of capstan lathes and millers, drills and polishers and hand-presses, worked by a multiplicity of belts and pulleys turning and twisting and slapping on heavy well-oiled wheels overhead, dependent for power on a motor stooping at the far end of the hall like the black shining bulk of a stranded whale. Machines with their own small motors started with a jerk and a whine under the shadows of their operators, increasing a noise that made the brain reel and ache because the weekend had been too tranquil by contrast, a weekend that had terminated for Arthur in fishing for trout in the cool shade of a willow-sleeved canal near the Balloon Houses, miles away from the city. Motor-trolleys moved up and down the main gangways carrying boxes of work—pedals, hubs, nuts and bolts—from one part of the shop to another. Robboe the foreman bent over a stack of new timesheets behind his glass partition; women and girls wearing turbans and hairnets and men and boys in clean blue overalls, settled down to their work, eager to get a good start on their day's stint; while sweepers and cleaners at everybody's beck and call already patrolled the gangways and looked busy.

Arthur reached his capstan lathe and took off his jacket, hanging it on a nearby nail so that he could keep an eye on his belongings. He pressed the starter button, and his motor came to life with a gentle thump. Looking around, it did not seem, despite the infernal noise of hurrying machinery, that anyone was working with particular speed. He smiled to himself and picked up a glittering steel cylinder from the top box of a pile beside him, and fixed it into the spindle. He jettisoned his cigarette into the sudpan, drew back the capstan, and swung the turret on to its broadest drill. Two minutes passed while he contemplated the precise position of tools and cylinder; finally he spat on to both hands and rubbed them together, then switched on the sud-tap from the movable brass pipe, pressed a button that set the spindle running, and ran in the drill to a neat chamfer. Monday morning had lost its terror.

Iris Murdoch

Iris Murdoch was born in Dublin of Anglo-Irish parents. She went to Badminton School, Bristol, and read classics at Somerville College, Oxford. During the war she worked at the Treasury. Miss Murdoch is now a Fellow and tutor in philosophy at St Anne's College, Oxford. Her novels are *Under the Net* (1954), *Flight from the Enchanter* (1956), *The Sandcastle* (1957), *The Bell* (1958), *A Severed Head* (1961), *The Unicorn* (1963) and *The Italian Girl* (1964). Miss Murdoch's theme is, perhaps, that though men and women may build fantasy worlds round themselves, life's difficulties and crises bring greater self-knowledge.

The Bell   The Butterfly

Michael Meade was aware of a strong vocation for the Church but homosexual tendencies had prevented his ordination. He has founded a lay religious community, near to a convent, at Imber, the Meade family's estate. His homosexuality is again to interfere with his plans.

Paul Greenfield, an art historian, is a guest of the lay community while working on manuscripts belonging to the convent. He is an unpleasant man, unbending, jealous and capable of violence. His wife Dora, an ex-art student, had left him some months earlier because she was afraid of him. Now she is returning to him. We meet her on the train travelling to Imber.

'Let me help you,' said a tall sunburnt man who was sitting opposite. He hoisted the big case easily on to the rack, and Dora threw Paul's hat up after it. The man smiled in a friendly way. They sat down. Everyone in this carriage was thinner.

Dora closed her eyes and remembered her fear. She was returning, and deliberately, into the power of someone whose conception of her life excluded or condemned her deepest urges and who now had good reason to judge her wicked. That was marriage, thought Dora; to be enclosed in the aims of another. That she had any power over Paul never occurred to her. It remained that her marriage to Paul was a fact, and one of the few

facts that remained in her disordered existence quite certain. She felt near
to tears and tried to think of something else.

The train was thundering through Maidenhead. Dora wished she
had got her book out of her suitcase before the train started. She felt too
shy to disturb her neighbour by doing so now. Anyway, the book was at
the bottom of the case and the whisky bottles on the top, so the situation
was best left alone. She began to study the other people in the carriage.
Some nondescript grey ladies, an elderly man, and opposite to her, two
younger men. Or rather, a man and a boy. The boy, who was sitting by
the window, must be about eighteen, and the man, who was the one who
had helped her with her luggage, about forty. These two appeared to be
travelling together. They were a good-looking pair. The man was large
and broad-shouldered, but a little gaunt and drawn in the face underneath his sunburn. He had an open friendly expression and a wide forehead crossed by rows of regular lines. He had plenty of curly dark brown
hair, going grey in places. His heavily veined hands were lightly clasped
on his knee, and his gaze shifted easily along the row of passengers opposite, appraising each without embarrassment. He had the sort of face which
can look full of amiability without smiling, and the sort of eyes which
can meet the eyes of a stranger and even linger, without seeming aggres-
sive, or seductive, or even curious. In spite of the heat of the day he was
dressed in heavy country tweeds. He wiped his perspiring forehead with a
clean handkerchief. Dora struggled out of her coat and thrust a hand
surreptitiously into her blouse to feel the perspiration collecting between
her breasts. She transferred her attention to the boy.

The boy sat in an attitude of very slightly self-conscious grace, one
long leg stretched out and almost touching Dora's. He wore dark grey
flannels and a white open-necked shirt. He had thrown his jacket into the
rack above. His sleeves were rolled up and his bare arm lay in the sun
along the dusty ledge of the window. He was less weather-beaten than his
companion but the recent sunshine had burnt his two cheeks to a dusky
red. He had an extremely round head with dark brown eyes, and his
dry hair, of a dull chestnut colour, which he kept a little long, fell in a
shell-like curve and ended in a clean line about his neck. He was very
slim and wore the wide-eyed insolent look of the happy person.

Dora recognized that look out of her own past as she contemplated the
boy, confident, unmarked, and glowing with health, his riches still in
store. Youth is a marvellous garment. How misplaced is the sympathy
lavished on adolescents. There is a yet more difficult age which comes

later, when one has less to hope for and less ability to change, when one has cast the die and has to settle into a chosen life without the consolations of habit or the wisdom of maturity, when, as in her own case, one ceases to be *une jeune fille un peu folle*, and becomes merely a woman, worst of all, a wife. The very young have their troubles, but they have at least a part to play, the part of being very young.

The pair opposite were talking, and Dora listened idly to their conversation.

'Must keep at your books, of course,' said the man. 'Mustn't let your maths get rusty before October.'

'I'll try,' said the boy. He behaved a little sheepishly to his companion. Dora wondered if they could be father and son, and decided that they were more likely to be master and pupil. There was something pedagogic about the older man.

'What an adventure for you young people,' said the man,' going up to Oxford! I bet you're excited?'

'Oh, *yes*,' said the boy. He answered quietly, a little nervous of a conversation in public. His companion had a loud booming voice and no one else was talking.

'I don't mind telling you, Toby, I envy you,' said the man. 'I didn't take that chance myself and I've regretted it all my life. At your age all I knew about was sailing boats!'

Toby, thought Dora. Toby Roundhead.

'Awfully lucky,' mumbled the boy.

Toby is trying to please his master, thought Dora. She took the last cigarette from her packet, and having peered inside several times to make sure that it was empty, threw the packet, after some indecision, out of the window, and caught a look of disapproval, immediately suppressed, on the face of the man opposite. She fumbled to tuck her blouse back into the top of her skirt. The afternoon seemed to be getting hotter.

'And what a splendid subject!' said the man. 'If you're an engineer you've got an honest trade that you can take with you anywhere in the world. It's the curse of modern life that people don't have real trades any more. A man is his work. In the old days we were all butchers and bakers and candlestick-makers, weren't we?'

'Yes,' said Toby. For some time now he had been conscious of Dora's stare. An anxious smile came and went upon his prominent and, it occurred to Dora, admirably red lips. He moved his leg nervously and his foot touched hers. He jerked back and tucked his feet under the seat. Dora was amused.

'That's one of the things we stand for,' said the man. 'To bring dignity and significance back into life through work. Too many people hate their work nowadays. That's why arts and crafts are so important. Even hobbies are important. Have you any hobbies?'

Toby was reticent.

Dora noticed some children standing on the embankment and waving at the train. She waved back, and found herself smiling. She caught Toby's eye; he began to smile too, but quickly looked away. As she continued to watch him he began to blush. Dora was delighted.

'A problem for our whole society,' the man was saying. 'But meanwhile, we have our individual lives to live, haven't we? And heaven help liberalism if that sense of individual vocation is ever lost. One must never be frightened of being called a crank. After all, there's an example to set, a way of keeping the problem before people's eyes, symbolically as it were. Don't you agree?'

Toby agreed.

The train began to slow down. 'Why, here we are in Oxford!' said the man. 'Look, Toby, there's your city!'

He pointed, and everyone in the carriage turned to look at a line of towers, silvered by the heat into a sky pale with light. Dora was suddenly reminded of travelling with Paul in Italy. She had accompanied him once on a non-stop trip to consult some manuscript. Paul detested being abroad. So, on that occasion, did Dora: barren lands made invisible by the sun, and poor starving cats driven away from expensive restaurants by waiters with flapping napkins. She remembered the towers of cities seen always from railway stations, with their fine names, Perugia, Parma, Piacenza. A strange nostalgic pain woke within her for a moment. Oxford, in the summer haze, looked no less alien. She had never been there. Paul was a Cambridge man.

The train had stopped now, but the pair opposite made no move. 'Yes, symbols are important,' said the man. 'Has it ever occurred to you that all symbols have a sacramental aspect? We do not live by bread alone. You remember what I told you about the bell?'

'Yes,' said Toby, showing interest. 'Will it come before I go?'

'Indeed it will,' said the man. 'It should be with us in a fortnight. We've planned a little ceremony, a sort of christening, all very picturesque and traditional. The Bishop has been very kind and agreed to come over. You'll be one of the exhibits, you know—the first of the few, or rather of the many. We hope to have a lot of you young people visiting us at Imber.'

Dora got up abruptly and stumbled in the direction of the corridor. Her face was glowing and she put up one hand to hide it. Her cigarette fell on the floor and she abandoned it. The train began to move again.

She could not have mis-heard the name. These two must be going to Imber as well, they must be members of that mysterious community Paul had spoken of. Dora leaned on the rail in the corridor. She fingered in her handbag for more cigarettes, and found she had left them in her coat pocket. She could not go back for them now. Behind her she could still hear the voices of Toby and his mentor, and it seemed suddenly as if they must be talking about her. For a short time they had existed for her diversion, but now they would be set before her as judges. Her acquaintance with them in the railway carriage had been something slight and fragile but at least innocent. The sweetness of these ephemeral contacts was precious to Dora. But now it was merely the prelude to some far drearier knowledge. It occurred to her to wonder how much Paul had said about her at Imber and what he had said. Her imagination, reeling still at the notion that Paul had actually existed during the months of their separation, now came to grips with the idea that he had not existed alone. Perhaps it was known that she was coming today. Perhaps the sunburnt man, who now seemed to look like a clergyman, had been on the lookout for the sort of woman who might be Paul's wife. Perhaps he had noticed her trying to catch Toby's eye. However had Paul described her?

Dora had a powerful imagination, at least in what concerned herself. She had long since recognized it as dangerous, and her talent was to send it, as she could her memory, to sleep. Now thoroughly roused it tormented her with pictures. The reality of the scene she was about to enter unfolded before her in rows of faces arrayed in judgement; and it seemed to Dora that the accusation which she had been prepared to receive from Paul would now be directed against her by every member of the already hateful community. She closed her eyes in indignation and distress. Why had she not thought of this? She was stupid and could see only one thing at a time. Paul had become a multitude.

She looked at her watch and realized with a shock that the train was due to arrive at Pendelcote in less than twenty minutes. Her heart began to beat in pain and pleasure at the thought of seeing Paul. It was necessary to return to the carriage. She powdered her nose, tucked her untidy blouse back again into her skirt, settled her collar, and plunged back towards her seat, keeping her head well down. Toby and his friend were still talking, but Dora murmured quiet imprecations to herself inside her head so that their words should not reach her. She looked resolutely at the floor, seeing a pair of heavy boots, and Toby's feet in sandals. A little time passed and the pain at her heart became more extreme.

Then Dora noticed that there was a Red Admiral butterfly walking on the dusty floor underneath the seat opposite. Every other thought left her head. Anxiously she watched the butterfly. It fluttered a little, and began to move towards the window, dangerously close to the passengers' feet. Dora held her breath. She ought to do something. But what? She flushed with indecision and embarrassment. She could not lean forward in front of all those people and pick the butterfly up in her hand. They would think her silly. It was out of the question. The sunburnt man, evidently struck with the concentration of Dora's gaze, bent down and fumbled with his boot laces. Both seemed securely tied. He shifted his feet, narrowly missing the butterfly which was now walking into the open on the carriage floor.

'Excuse me,' said Dora. She knelt down and gently scooped the creature into the palm of her hand, and covered it over with her other hand. She could feel it fluttering inside. Everyone stared. Dora blushed violently. Toby and his friend were looking at her in a friendly surprised way. Whatever should she do now? If she put the butterfly out of the window it would be sucked into the whirlwind of the train and killed. Yet she could not just go on holding it, it would look too idiotic. She bowed her head, pretending to examine her captive.

The train was slowing down. With horror Dora realized that it must be Pendelcote. Toby and his companion were gathering their luggage together. Already the station was appearing. The other two were moving towards the door as the train jolted to a standstill. Dora stood up, her hands still cupped together. She must get herself out of the train. She quickly thrust one hand through the handles of her handbag and the canvas bag, and closed it again above the now quiescent butterfly. Then she began to totter towards the carriage door. People were beginning to get into the train. Dora backed her way out, pushing vigorously, keeping the butterfly cupped safely against her chest. She managed to get down the steep step on to the platform without falling, although her awkward shoes leaned over sideways at the heels. She righted herself and stood there looking round. She was on the open part of the platform and the sunlight rose from the glinting concrete and dazzled her eyes. For a moment she could see nothing. The train began to move slowly away.

Then with a deep shock she saw Paul coming towards her. His real presence glowed to her, striking her heart again, and she felt both afraid and glad to see him. He was a little changed, thinner and browned by the sun, and the blazing afternoon light revealed him to her in the splendour of his Southern look and his slightly Edwardian handsomeness. He was not smiling but looking at her very intently with a narrow stare of anxious suspicion. His dark moustache drooped with his sourly curving mouth. For a second Dora felt happy that she had done at least one thing to please him. She had come back. But the next instant, as he came up to her, all was anxiety and fear.

Paul was followed closely by Toby and his companion, who had evidently met him further down the platform. Dora could see them smiling at her over Paul's shoulder. She turned to him.

'Well, Dora——' said Paul.

'Hello,' said Dora.

Toby's companion said, 'Well met! I do wish we'd known who you were. I'm afraid we quite left you out of the conversation! We travelled up with your wife, but we didn't realize it was her.'

'May I introduce,' said Paul, 'James Tayper Pace. And this is Toby Gashe. I've got your name right, I hope? My wife.'

They stood in a group together in the sun, their shadows intermingled. The other travellers had gone.

'So very glad to meet you!' said James Tayper Pace.

'Hello,' said Dora.

'Where's your luggage?' said Paul.

'My God!' said Dora. Her mouth flew open. She had left the suitcase on the train.

'You left it on the train?' said Paul.

Dora nodded dumbly.

'Typical, my dear,' said Paul. 'Now let's go to the car.' He stopped. 'Was my notebook in it?'

'Yes,' said Dora. 'I'm terribly sorry.'

'You'll get it back,' said James. 'Folk are honest.'

'That's not my experience,' said Paul. His face was harshly closed. 'Now come along. Why are you holding your hands like that?' he said to Dora. 'Are you praying, or what?'

Dora had forgotten about the butterfly. She opened her hands now, holding the wrists together and opening the palms like a flower. The brilliantly coloured butterfly emerged. It circled round them for a moment and then fluttered across the sunlit platform and flew away into the distance. There was a moment's surprised silence.

'You are full of novelties,' said Paul.

They followed him in the direction of the exit.

V S Naipaul

V. S. Naipaul was born in Trinidad in 1932. He was educated at Queens Royal College, Trinidad, and came to University College, Oxford, when he was eighteen. Mr Naipaul is the grandson of an Indian immigrant who settled in Trinidad and his first four novels are mostly concerned with the Hindu community there; these are *The Mystic Masseur* (1957), *The Suffrage of Elvira* (1958), *Miguel Street* (1959) and *A House for Mr Biswas* (1961). *The Middle Passage*, published in 1962, is an account of a visit to the Caribbean after ten years' absence. Mr Naipaul's first novel with an English setting was *Mr Stone and the Knights Companion*, which appeared in 1963. *An Area of Darkness* (1964) is an account of his first visit to India; he spent a year there. *The Minute Men*, a novel, was published in 1967.

Mr Naipaul has in abundance the novelist's gifts of insight and the ability to communicate what he has seen. He knows that the truth about even a single human life is complex; with compassion and delicacy and often with humour he reveals to us the human situation. Something else. Novels are unique in their power to convey the quality of life in a town, a village, a district, a country; Mr Naipaul's fiction makes Trinidad accessible to the English reader.

A House for Mr Biswas   English Composition

This book is an account of the attempts of Mohun Biswas to achieve independence and to make his mark. The constant use of the title 'Mr' is not scornful or facetious but, because the book is written from a deep compassion, a constant and poignant reminder of his human dignity. 'Born unnecessary and unaccommodated' he lived in poverty all the forty-six years of his life. His body was shaped by malnutrition. He always lived in squalor in crowded rooms and houses. Mr Biswas's problem was not just to live, but first of all to make for himself a world to live in: his family was Hindu and still observed Hindu customs and religious practices; he attended a Canadian Mission school where the teacher 'had been converted to Presbyterianism from a low Hindu caste and held all unconverted Hindus in contempt'; at school he learned to say the Lord's Prayer in Hindi and he learned many English poems by heart from the Royal Reader; *American magazines entered the island and syndicated columns like* That Body of Yours *which dealt every day with a different danger to the human body appeared in the island's papers. When Mr. Biswas was very young he married into the overwhelming Tulsi family. Mr. Biswas came to believe that his life would have significance if only he had a house of his own. A few days before he died he became the owner of a shoddy house. It was sold to him by a swindler. 'Living had always been a preparation, a waiting. And so the years had passed; and now there was nothing to wait for.' When he died the house was full of mourners. 'The polished floor became scratched and dusty; the staircase shivered continually: the top floor resounded with the steady shuffle. And the house did not fall.' Mr Biswas had made his mark. He was remembered. For several years Mr Biswas was a reporter, at fifteen dollars a fortnight, on* The Sentinel. *He had a sense of ironic comedy and an English style ('Amazing scenes were witnessed. . . . ') which suited the editor of this sensational newspaper. His wife was called Shama and his son Anand. Owad and Shekhar were his brothers-in-law. Fish and prunes were regarded as brain food.*

Sunday brought the *Sunday Sentinel* and Mr Biswas's scandalous feature, 'I Am Trinidad's Most Evil Man', one of a series of interviews with Trinidad's richest, poorest, tallest, fattest, thinnest, strongest men; which was following a series on men with unusual callings: thief, beggar, night-soil remover, mosquito-killer, undertaker, birth-certificate searcher, lunatic asylum warden; which had followed a series on one-armed, one-legged, one-eyed men; which had come about when, after a Mr Biswas interview with a man who had been shot years before in the neck and had to cover up the hole in order to speak, the *Sentinel* office had been crowded with men with interesting mutilations, offering to sell their story.

Mr Biswas's article was hilariously received by Owad and Shekhar, particularly as the most evil man was a well-known Arwacas character. He had committed one murder under great provocation and after his acquittal had developed into a genial bore. The title of the interview promised for the following week, with Trinidad's maddest man, aroused further laughter.

After breakfast all the men—and this included Anand—went for a bathe at the harbour extension at Docksite. The dredging was incomplete, but the sea-wall had been built and in the early morning parts of the sea provided safe, clean bathing, though at every footstep the mud rose, clouding the water. The reclaimed land, raised to the level of the sea-wall, was not as yet real land, only crusted mud, sharp among the cracks which patterned it like a coral fan.

The sun was not out and the high, stationary clouds were touched with red. Ships were blurred in the distance; the level sea was like dark glass. Anand was left at the edge of the water, near the wall, and the men went ahead, their voices and splashings carrying far in the stillness. All at once the sun came out, the water blazed, the sounds were subdued.

Aware of his unimpressive physique, Mr Biswas began to clown; and as he did more and more now, he tried to extend his clowning to Anand.

'Duck, boy!' he called. 'Duck and let us see how long you can stay under water.'

'No!' Anand shouted back.

This abrupt denial of his father's authority had become part of the clowning.

'You hear the boy?' Mr Biswas said to Owad and Shekhar. He spoke an obscene Hindi epigram which had always amused them and which they now associated with him.

'You know what I feel like doing?' he said a little later.' See that rowing-boat there, by the wall? Let us untie it. By tomorrow morning it will be in Venezuela.'

'And let us throw you in it,' Shekhar said.

They chased Mr Biswas, caught him, held him above the water while he laughed and squirmed, his calves swinging like hammocks.

'One,' they counted, swinging him. 'Two——'

Suddenly he became affronted and angry.

'Three!'

The smooth water slapped his belly and chest and forehead like something hard and hot. Surfacing, his back to them, he took some time to rearrange his hair, in reality wiping away the tears that had come to his eyes. The pause was long enough to tell Owad and Shekhar that he was angry. They were embarrassed; and he was recognizing the unreasonableness of his anger when Shekhar said, 'Where is Anand?'

Mr Biswas didn't turn. 'The boy all right. Ducking. His grandfather was a champion diver.'

Owad laughed.

'Ducking, hell!' Shekhar said, and began swimming towards the wall.

There was no sign of Anand. In the shadow of the wall the rowingboat barely rocked above its reflection.

Silently Mr Biswas and Owad watched Shekhar. He dived. Mr Biswas scooped up a handful of water and let it fall on his head. Some of it ran down his face; some of it sprinkled the sea.

Shekhar re-appeared near the sea-wall, shook the water from his head and dived again.

Mr Biswas began to wade towards the wall. Owad began to swim. Mr Biswas began to swim.

Shekhar surfaced again, near the rowingboat. There was alarm on his face. He was holding Anand under his left arm and was pulling strongly with his right.

Owad and Mr Biswas pulled towards him. He shouted to them to keep away. All at once he stopped pulling with his right hand, stood up, and was only waist-high in water. Behind him, in shadow, the rowingboat barely moved.

They carried Anand to the top of the wall and rolled him. Then Shekhar did some kneading exercises on his thin back. Mr Biswas stood by, noticing only the large safetypin—one of Shama's, doubtless—on Anand's blue striped shirt, which lay in the small heap of his clothes.

Anand spluttered. His expression was one of anger. He said, 'I was walking to the boat.'

'I told you to stay where you were,' Mr Biswas said, angry too.

'And the bottom of the sea drop away.'

'The dredging,' Shekhar said. He had not lost his look of alarm.

'The sea just drop away,' Anand cried, lying on his back, covering his face with a crooked arm. He spoke as one insulted.

Owad said, 'Anyway, you've got the record for ducking, Shompo.'

'Shut up!' Anand screamed. He began to cry, rubbing his legs on the hard, cracked ground, then turning over on his belly.

Mr Biswas took up his shirt with the safetypin and handed it to Anand.

Anand snatched his shirt and said, 'Leave me.'

'We shoulda leave you,' Mr Biswas said, 'when you was there, ducking.' As soon as he spoke the last word he regretted it.

'Yes!' Anand screamed. 'You shoulda leave me.' He got up and, going to his heap of clothes, began to dress furiously, forcing his clothes over his wet and gritty skin. 'I am never going to come out with any of you again.' His eyes were small and red, the lids swollen.

He walked away from them, quickly, his small body silhouetted against the sun, across the weed-ridden mud flat. Unused, his towel remained rolled, a large bundle below his arm.

'Well,' Mr Biswas said. 'Back for a little duck?'

Owad and Shekhar smiled. Then, slowly, they all dressed.

'I never thought the day would come when I would be glad that I was a sea scout,' Shekhar said. 'It was just like a hole in the sea, you know. And there was a helluva pull. By tomorrow little Anand would really have been in Venezuela.'

They found Shama anxious to know why Anand had been sent back. He had said nothing and had locked himself in his room.

Savi and Myna burst into tears when they heard.

The lunch was the climax of the week-end festivities, but Anand did not come out of his room. He ate only a slice of water melon which Savi took to him.

Later that afternoon, after Shekhar had left, Shama gave vent to her annoyance. Anand had spoiled the week-end for everybody and she was going to flog him. She was dissuaded only by Owad's pleas.

'My children! My children!' Shama said. 'Well, the example set. They just following.'

The next day Mr Biswas wrote an angry article about the lack of warning notices at Docksite. In the afternoon Anand came home from school a little more composed and, extraordinarily, without being asked, took a copy book out from his bag and handed it to Mr Biswas, who was in the hammock in the back verandah. Then Anand went to change.

The copy book contained Anand's English compositions, which reflected the vocabulary and ideals of Anand's teacher as well as Anand's obsession with the stylistic device of the noun followed by a dash, an adjective and the noun again: for example, 'the robbers—the ruthless robbers'.

The last composition was headed 'A Day by the Seaside'. Below that the phrases supplied by the teacher had been copied down: project a visit—feverish preparations—eager anticipation—laden hampers—wind blowing through open car—spirits overflowing into song—graceful curve of coconut trees—arc of golden sand—crystalline water—pounding surf—majestic rollers—energetically battling the waves—cries of delirious joy—grateful shade of coconut trees—glorious sunset—sad to leave— memory to be cherished in future days—looking forward in eager antici- pation to paying a return visit.

Mr Biswas was familiar with the clarity and optimism of the teacher's vision, and he expected Anand to write: 'With anticipation—eager anti- cipation—we projected a visit to the seaside and we made preparations— feverish preparations—and then on the appointed morning we struggled with hampers—laden hampers—into the motorcar.' For in these composi- tions Anand and his fellows knew nothing but luxury.

But in his last composition there were no dashes and repetitions; no hampers, no motor car, no golden arms of sand; only a walk to Docksite, a concrete sea-wall and liners in the distance. Mr Biswas read on, anxious to share the pain of the previous day. 'I raised my hand but I did not know if it got to the top. I opened my mouth to cry for help. Water filled it. I thought I was going to die and I closed my eyes because I did not want to look at the water.' The composition ended with a denunciation of the sea.

None of the teacher's phrases had been used but the composition had been given twelve marks out of ten.

Anand had come back to the verandah and was having his tea at the table.

Mr Biswas wished to be close to him. He would have done anything to make up for the solitude of the previous day. He said, 'Come and sit down here and go through the composition with me.'

Anand became impatient. He was pleased by the marks but was fed up with the composition and even a little ashamed of it. He had been made to read it out to the class, and the confession that he had not strug- gled with laden hampers into a car and driven to palm-fringed beaches but had walked to common Docksite had caused some laughter. So had the sentences: 'I opened my mouth to cry for help. Water filled it.'

'Come,' Mr Biswas said, making room in the hammock.

'No!' Anand shouted.

But there was no one to laugh.

Mr Biswas's hurt turned to anger. 'Go and cut me a whip,' he said, getting out of the hammock. 'Go on. Quick sharp.'

Anand stamped down the back stairs. From the neem tree that grew at the edge of the lot and hung over into the sewerage trace he cut a thick rod, far thicker than those he normally cut. His purpose was to insult Mr Biswas. Mr Biswas recognized the insult and was further enraged. He seized the rod and beat Anand savagely. In the end Shama had to intervene.

'I can't stand this,' Savi said. 'I can't stand you people. I am going back to Hanuman House.'

Myna was crying as well.

Shama said to Anand, 'You see what you cause?'

He said nothing.

'Good!' Savi said. 'All this shouting and screaming make this house sound like every other house in the street. I hope the low minds of some people are satisfied.'

'Yes,' Mr Biswas said calmly. 'Some people are satisfied.'

His smile drove Savi to fresh tears.

But Anand had his revenge that evening.

Now that there were only a few days left to Owad in Trinidad, and very few before the family came to Port of Spain for the farewell, Mr Biswas and Anand ate as many meals as possible with him. They ate formally, in the diningroom. And that evening, just before Mr Biswas sat at the table, Anand pulled the chair from under him, and Mr Biswas fell noisily to the floor.

'Shompo! Lompo! Gomp!' Owad said, roaring with laughter.

Savi said, 'Well, some people are satisfied.'

Mr Biswas didn't talk during the meal. Afterwards he went for a walk. When he came back he went directly to his room and never once called to anyone to get his cigarettes or matches or books.

It was his habit to walk through the house at six in the morning, rustling the newspaper and getting everyone up. Then he himself went back to bed: he had the gift of enjoying sleep in snatches. He woke no one the next morning and didn't show himself while the children were getting ready for school.

But before Anand left, Shama gave him a six-cents piece.

'From your father. For milk from the Dairies.'

At three that afternoon, when school was over, Anand walked down Victoria Avenue, past the racketing wheels and straps of the Government Printery, crossed Tragarete Road for the shade of the ivy-covered walls of Lapeyrouse Cemetery, and turned into Phillip Street where, in the cigarette factory, was the source of the sweet smell of tobacco which hung over the district. The Dairies looked expensive and forbidding in white and pale green. Anand tiptoed to the caged desk, said to the woman, 'A small bottle of milk please,' paid, got his voucher, and sat on a tall pale green stool at the milky-smelling bar. The white-capped barman tried to stab off the silver top a little too nonchalantly and, failing twice, pressed it out with a large thumb. Anand didn't care for the ice-cold milk and the cloying sweetness it left at the back of his throat; it also seemed to have the tobacco smell, which he associated with the cemetery.

When he got home Shama gave him a small brown paper parcel. It contained prunes. They were his, to eat as and when he pleased.

Both he and Savi were told to keep the milk and the prunes secret, lest Owad should hear of it and laugh at them for their presumptuousness.

And almost immediately Anand began to pay the price of the milk and prunes. Mr Biswas went to the school and saw the headmaster and the teacher whose vocabulary he knew so well. They agreed that Anand could win an exhibition if he worked, and Mr Biswas made arrangements for Anand to be given private lessons after school, after milk. To balance this, Mr Biswas also arranged for Anand to have unlimited credit at the school shop; thus deranging Shama's accounts further.

Savi's heart went out to Anand.

'I am too glad,' she said, 'that God didn't give me a brain.'

Further selected readings : English

H. G. WELLS: *The First Men in the Moon.* 1901
Chapter 12. Cavor, the inventor, and Bedford, who tells the story, have landed on the moon and been taken prisoner by the Selenites.

JOHN GALSWORTHY: *The Man of Property.* 1906
Part Two, Chapter 14, 'Soames sits on the stairs'. Is Soames Forsyte's wife also his property?

H. G. WELLS: *Tono-Bungay.* 1908
Collins edition, p. 124, 'His proposal . . .' to p. 128, '. . . "I'll think it over" '.
Uncle Edward Ponderevo has concocted a patent medicine which is 'selling like hot cakes'.

ARNOLD BENNETT: *Clayhanger.* 1910
Book One, Chapters 4 and 5. Darius Clayhanger starts work and lives through a shameful experience.
Book One, Chapter 14. His son Edwin is aware of a sense of vocation.

ROBERT TRESSALL: *The Ragged-Trousered Philanthropists.* 1914
Chapter 8, 'The Long Hill'. Mainly about Bert, a boy who sat down in the boss's time.

NAOMI MITCHISON: *The Conquered.* 1923
Chapter 4, 'Would it, after all, be possible to escape?' to the end of the chapter (Cape edition, pp. 83–94). Meromic was the son of a chief of the Veneti in Brittany in 56 BC. When his people had been beaten and his sister had killed herself, Meromic decided to surrender to the Romans.

VIRGINIA WOOLF: *To the Lighthouse.* 1927
Chapter 5. Mrs Ramsay and six-year-old James, who is looking forward to the visit to the lighthouse.

T. F. POWYS: *Mr Weston's Good Wine.* 1927
Chapter 16. The Reverend Nicholas Grobe, Vicar of Folly Down, liked the long hours of a winter's evening.

EVELYN WAUGH: *Decline and Fall.* 1928
Chapters 2 and 3. Paul Pennyfeather takes up his first teaching appointment.

J. B. PRIESTLEY: *The Good Companions.* 1929
The first three paragraphs. Zooming down on Bruddersford. Heinemann edition, p. 18, 'The week-end had begun badly . . .' to p. 23, '. . . as far as that.' Jess Oakroyd had been down South.

W. SOMERSET MAUGHAM: *Cakes and Ale.* 1930
Chapter 5. The first Mrs Driffield.

WALTER GREENWOOD: *Love on the Dole.* 1933
Part Three, Chapter 4, 'Musical Chairs'. Harry Hardcastle had looked forward to finishing his apprenticeship and earning forty-nine shillings a week.

ANTHONY POWELL: *From a View to a Death.* 1933
Penguin edition, pp. 7–14. Why Arthur Zouch was glad to be invited to Passenger Court.

ROSE MACAULAY: *Going Abroad.* 1934
Chapter 21. A party of visitors staying near San Sebastian is kidnapped while making a journey inland to see Loyola, the birthplace of Saint Ignatius.

ELIZABETH BOWEN: *The Death of the Heart.* 1938
Chapter 2. 'It was five to four. . .' to '"Do you mind", he said, "if I just have a look at this?" ' Penguin edition, pp. 24–33. Portia Quayle is sixteen years old and an orphan. Her half-brother and her sister-in-law provide shelter, but not affection.

CHRISTOPHER ISHERWOOD: *Goodbye to Berlin.* 1939
Penguin edition, pp. 19–23. The first private pupil.

JOYCE CARY: *The Horse's Mouth.* 1944
The first two chapters. Gulley Jimson, artist, has been in prison for a month and goes to inspect his studio by the Thames.

ALAN PATON: *Cry, the Beloved Country.* 1948
Book One, Chapter 2. The Reverend Stephen Kumalo and his wife receive a letter from Johannesburg.

GEORGE ORWELL: *Nineteen Eighty-Four.* 1949
Part One, Chapter 1. Winston Smith begins to keep a diary; the Two Minutes Hate. Penguin edition, pp. 5–11; 11–19.

DORIS LESSING: *The Grass is Singing.* 1950
Penguin edition, p. 78 to p. 84, '. . . against all natives.' A permissible outlet? Mary Turner, a town girl now married to a farmer, receives her first visitors, Mr and Mrs Slatter.

JOHN WAIN: *Hurry on Down.* 1953
Chapter 8, 'The man in the white coat . . .' to '. . . and they were inside.' Penguin edition, pp. 169–76. An unexpectedly bitter row about Reilly's monocle and a decent game like rugger.

ANGUS WILSON: *Anglo-Saxon Attitudes.* 1956
Chapter 3, to '. . . when she said goodbye.' Mrs Salad collects her Christmas present.

STANLEY MIDDLETON: *Harris's Requiem.* 1960
Chapter 9. Blidworth Band plays Thomas Harris's Blidworth March.

Selected readings from American fiction

HENRY JAMES: *The Turn of the Screw.* 1898
The narrator's introduction. 'The story had held us . . .'

THEODORE DREISER: *Sister Carrie.* 1900
Chapter 3. A job in Chicago.

UPTON SINCLAIR: *The Jungle.* 1906
Penguin edition, p. 30, 'It was in the stockyards . . .' to p. 38. Chicago; the end of the journey from Lithuania.

WILLA CATHER: *My Ántonia.* 1918
Chapters 1–3. Jim Burden and Ántonia Shimerdas reach Nebraska on the same day: Jim from Virginia, Ántonia from Bohemia.

SHERWOOD ANDERSON: *Winesburg, Ohio.* 1919
'Queer'. Elmer Cowley would show people that he could make friends and be happy like other people.

SINCLAIR LEWIS: *Babbitt.* 1922
Chapter 1. Mr and Mrs George F. Babbitt of Floral Heights, Zenith.

F. SCOTT FITZGERALD: *The Great Gatsby,* 1925.
Penguin edition, Chapter 3 to p. 54. A week-end party at Gatsby's home on Long Island.

JOHN O'HARA: *Appointment in Samarra.* 1934
Chapter 1, section 2. Christmas Eve at the country club.

JOHN STEINBECK: *Of Mice and Men.* 1937
Penguin edition, p. 7 to p. 13, '. . . and then went on whistling again.' George and Lennie.

ERNEST HEMINGWAY: *First Forty-nine Short Stories.* 1938
A story like 'The Battler' is an excellent introduction to Hemingway the novelist.

JOHN P. MARQUAND: *Wickford Point*. 1939
Collins edition, p. 7, 'I must you know' to p. 10. An invitation from a successful author.
P. 33, 'When Aunt Sarah was seventeen . . .' to p. 35. An incident in family history.

THOMAS WOLFE: *You Can't Go Home Again*. 1940
Chapter 33, 'Enter Mr Lloyd McHarg'. George Webber, who has written a book, meets a famous author and a publisher.

CARSON MCCULLERS: *The Heart is a Lonely Hunter*. 1940
Cresset Press edition, Chapter 3, pp. 25–31. Mick's Sunday morning walk (Mick is a girl).

WILLIAM FAULKNER: *The Collected Short Stories*, Vol. I. 1942
A short story would serve as an introduction, e.g. 'Two Soldiers'.

VLADIMIR NABOKOV: *Bend Sinister*. 1947
Weidenfeld and Nicolson edition, p. 43, 'They were interrupted by the President . . .' to p. 53, '. . . nodded to Doctor Azureus.' Adam Krug, a world-famous philosopher, refuses to sign and deliver the university's profession of loyalty to the Ruler.

J. D. SALINGER: *The Catcher in the Rye*. 1951
Penguin edition, Chapter 16, first four pages; and Chapter 17, first six pages. It seems to Holden Caulfield, who is seventeen, that the world is full of phonies.

MARY MCCARTHY: *The Groves of Academe*. 1953
Chapter 1, 'An Unexpected Letter'.

JAMES BALDWIN: *Go Tell it on the Mountain*. 1954
Corgi edition, p. 193, 'She had made her great mistake . . .' to p. 200, '. . . not to tell him yet about the child.' Elizabeth remembers Richard's last days.

SAUL BELLOW: *Seize the Day*. 1956
Penguin edition, p. 18, 'There was the matter of the different names . . .' to p. 27, 'It would kill me to go back to school now.' The screen test.

JOHN UPDIKE: *Rabbit Run*. 1960
The first six pages. Harry ('Rabbit') Angstrom, once successful as a high school baseball player, joins in a street game with some boys, but has to go home to his wife.

JOHN DOS PASSOS: *Midcentury*. 1961
André Deutsch edition, pp. 479–86. James Dean.

Selected readings in translation

FYODOR DOSTOEVSKY: *Letters from the Underworld*. Russia, 1864
  The first chapter of the story 'The Gentle Maiden'. Who We Were.

COLETTE: *Claudine at School*. France, 1900
  Penguin edition, p. 11, 'Two months ago . . .' to p. 19, '. . . with the jealous eyes.' Claudine is to have English lessons with the new mistress.

THOMAS MANN: *Death in Venice*. Germany, 1913
  Penguin edition, p. 33, 'The weather next day . . .' to p. 40, '. . . the pleasure the idea gave him.' Gustave Aschenbach is obsessed by the beauty of Tadzio, a Polish boy.

MARCEL PROUST: *Swann's Way*. France, 1913
  Chatto and Windus paperback, p. 98, 'But if the thought of actors . . .' to p. 106, '. . . not one of us ever set eyes on him again.' The lady in pink.

ANDRÉ GIDE: *The Vatican Cellars*. France, 1914
  Penguin edition, p. 168 to p. 177, '. . . Lafcadio bowed.' The meeting with Lafcadio Wluiki.

FRANZ KAFKA: 'The Metamorphosis' (short story). Czechoslovakia, 1916
  Penguin edition, from the beginning to p. 21, '. . . his great chest heaved'. Gregor Samsa wakes up to find himself transformed into a giant insect. How is he to get up, and to explain his absence from work?

JAROSLAV HAŠEK: *The Good Soldier Schweik*. Czechoslovakia, 1921
  Penguin edition, pp. 197–206. Schweik obtains a dog for Lieutenant Lukash; but the consequences are unfortunate.

ITALO SVEVO: *The Confessions of Zeno*. Italy, 1923
  Penguin edition, p. 79, 'I married his daughter.' to p. 87, 'They begged me to stay on and offered me a cup of tea.' The family Zeno married into.

COLETTE: *Ripening Seed*. France, 1923
  Chapter 1. Philippe and Vinca were childhood friends.

RICARDO GUIRALDES: *Don Segundo Sombra; Shadows on the Pampas*. Argentina, 1926
  Chapters 1 and 2 and the first paragraph of 3 (Penguin edition, pp. 3–16). Fabio meets Don Segundo. He is fascinated by his calm strength and decides to follow him.

MIKHAIL SHOLOKHOV: *And Quiet Flows the Don*. Russia, 1926
  Part 1, Chapter 2, section 1. Here we meet Gregor, son of the Melekhov family, who live in the Cossack village of Tatarsk on the River Don. The time is just before 1914.
  Part 1, Chapter 9, section 4. A stranger from Rostov, called Stockman, comes to live in the village, hoping to make a living as a locksmith and carpenter.

Selected readings in translation

ARNOLD ZWEIG: *The Case of Sergeant Grischa.* Germany, 1927
Book 1, Chapter 2: 'Escape!' In March 1917 Sergeant Grischa, a Russian, escapes from a German prisoner-of-war camp in Poland.

ERICH MARIA REMARQUE: *All Quiet on the Western Front.* Germany, 1929
Mayflower-Dell paperback edition, pp. 21–3, Corporal Himmelstoss; p. 36, 'Meanwhile Haie . . .' to p. 38: Revenge; pp. 46–7: Horses.

IGNAZIO SILONE: *Fontamara.* Italian but published in Switzerland, 1933
Penguin edition, Chapter 2 to p. 30, '. . . arrived from Rome yesterday'. A matter for the mayor. Period: 1922–30.

ANDRÉ MALRAUX: *Man's Estate.* France, 1933
Part 1. March 21st 1927; 12.30 a.m. Chen believes that, for the Revolution, even murder can be justified.

ANTOINE DE SAINT-EXUPÉRY: *Wind, Sand and Stars.* France, 1939
Heinemann edition, p. 3 to p. 10, '. . . of night flight.' The mail pilot is briefed for his first flight, in 1926.

ALBERT CAMUS: *The Outsider.* France, 1942
Penguin edition, pp. 93–8. Céleste, a café proprietor, is witness at the trial of Meursault.

CESARE PAVESE: *The Devil in the Hills.* Italy, 1948
Chapter 1. On summer nights the three friends could not bring themselves to go to bed.

JEAN-PAUL SARTRE: *Nausea.* France, 1938
Penguin edition, pp. 24–6. The subject of Antoine Roquentin's book. P. 35, 'Madeleine . . .' to p. 38, '. . . the Nausea vanished.' At the café.

HEINRICH BÖLL: *The Train was on Time.* Germany, 1949
Sphere Books, paperback edition, p. 38, 'It suddenly occurred to Andreas that they were already in Poland', to p. 43, '. . . Why torment his weary legs any more?' On the train going back from leave to the Russian front, Andreas is sure that he will be killed. He thinks of Germany, and of a girl he saw briefly when he was serving in France.

SAMUEL BECKETT: *Molloy.* France, 1950
Jupiter Books edition, p. 34, 'For I had hardly perfected my plan . . .' to p. 37, '. . . was not far away.' Molloy has an accident. P. 62, 'But I left Lousse at last . . .' to p. 64, '. . . I have been there all the time.' Molloy is on his way again.

BORIS PASTERNAK: *Doctor Zhivago.* Russian, but published in Western Europe, 1958, Chapter 12, section 9. Dr Yury Zhivago has been captured by the Bolshevik partisans and made to serve as their medical officer. At this point he has already been with them eighteen months.

Modern Novelists

GIUSEPPE DI LAMPEDUSA: *The Leopard*. Italy, 1958
Collins Fontana edition, p. 85, 'For the moment . . .' to p. 87, '. . . were dozing off'. P. 97, ' "Listen, Don Ciccio. . . ." ' to p. 102, 'Sancho Panza.' The Prince and Don Ciccio are out shooting. The Prince is asking about Angelica, whom his own nephew, Tancredi, wants to marry.

GUNTER GRASS: *The Tin Drum*. Germany, 1959
Penguin edition, p. 71, 'The school board expressed misgivings . . .' to p. 79, '. . . My First School Day.' Oskar demoralizes Miss Spollenhauer and Class IA at the Pestalozzi School.

Books on the modern novel

WALTER ALLEN: *The English Novel*. 1954
Tradition and Dream. 1964

MIRIAM ALLOTT: *Novelists on the Novel*. 1959

LESLIE FIEDLER: *Waiting for the End: The American Literary Scene from Hemingway to Baldwin*. 1965

G. S. FRASER: *The Modern Writer and his World*. 1964

F. R. LEAVIS: *The Great Tradition: George Eliot, Henry James, Joseph Conrad*. 1948

Q. V. LEAVIS: *Fiction and the Reading Public*. 1932

MARK SCHORER: *Modern British Fiction*. 1961

PAUL WEST: *The Modern Novel*. 1963

EDMUND WILSON: *Axel's Castle*. 1931